Human Body

PRENTICE HALL GENERAL REFERENCE
15 Columbus Circle
New York, New York 10023

PRENTICE HALL and colophon are registered trademarks of
Simon & Schuster Inc.

Designed by Jane Brett and Steven Hulbert
Manufactured in Great Britain by BPCC Hazells Ltd.

Originally published in Great Britain by Merlion Publishing Ltd. as
THE ILLUSTRATED DICTIONARY OF THE HUMAN BODY in a
different form.

A Prentice Hall Illustrated Dictionary

Human Body

Contributors
Mal Sainsbury
Merilyn Holme
Josephine Paker

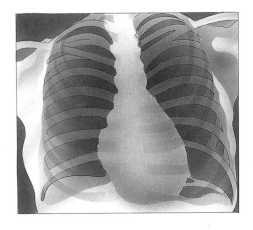

PRENTICE HALL GENERAL REFERENCE
New York · London · Toronto · Sydney · Tokyo · Singapore

Reader's notes

The entries in this dictionary have several features to help you broaden your understanding of the word you are looking up.

- Each entry is introduced by its headword. All the headwords in the dictionary are arranged in alphabetical order.

- Each headword is followed by a part of speech to show whether the word is used as a noun, adjective, verb, or prefix.

- Each entry begins with a sentence that uses the headword as its subject.

- Words that are bold in an entry are cross references. You can look them up in this dictionary to find out more information about the topic.

- Many of the entries are accompanied by illustrations. The labels on the illustrations highlight the key points of information and will help you to understand some of the science behind the entries.

- Many of the labels on the illustrations have their own entries in the dictionary and can therefore be used as cross references.

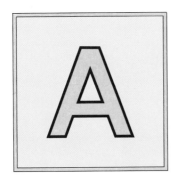

abdomen   *noun*
The abdomen is the large area between the **chest** and the **pelvis**. It contains many important **organs**, such as the **stomach**, the **intestines**, the **spleen**, and the **liver**. These organs are wrapped in a thin lining called the **peritoneum**. A large muscle called the **diaphragm** lies across the top of these organs and separates them from the **lungs**.
The front of the abdomen is made of layers of muscle.

abscess   *noun*
An abscess is an **infection** that is a red, swollen lump filled with **pus**. It builds up in tissue that is infected with **bacteria**, and it can develop at any place in the body. The pus in an abscess contains dead **white blood cells**, which fight the bacteria.
The abscess on her gum made her face swell.

absorption   *noun*
Absorption is the process by which body tissue takes in other substances. Food is broken down and absorbed in the **stomach** and **intestines**, and nutrients are carried in the bloodstream to all parts of the body.
Oxygen is absorbed from the lungs into the bloodstream.
absorb   *verb*

Achilles' tendon   *noun*
The Achilles' tendon is the thick **tendon** at the back of the ankle. It attaches the calf muscles to the bone of the heel.
His Achilles' tendon was injured while he was playing football.

acid   *noun*
An acid is a substance that reacts with a base to form a salt. The stomach produces acid which breaks down and helps **digest** food.
Stomach acid kills some germs in food.

acne   *noun*
Acne is a skin disorder that occurs when the **sebaceous glands** in the skin become infected. The sebaceous glands produce an oil called **sebum**, which comes out onto the surface of the skin through the pores. If the pores are blocked, an infection builds up inside the sebaceous glands. Acne often starts when the **hormones** produced during puberty make the sebaceous glands produce more sebum.
He used a medical ointment to treat his acne.

acupuncture   *noun*
Acupuncture is a way of preventing and treating illness and relieving pain. For acupuncture, fine needles are inserted into different points on the body. In China, acupuncture is sometimes used instead of an **anesthetic**, to block pain during an **operation**. The patient stays awake but seems to feel little or no pain.
Acupuncture can help to relieve back pain.

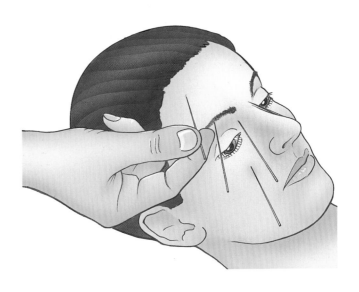

acute *adjective*
An acute illness or pain is one that develops suddenly or suddenly becomes worse. The opposite of acute is **chronic**.
She felt acute pain in her ankle after she twisted it.

Adam's apple ► **larynx**

adenoids *noun*
The adenoids are glandular tissue that is found inside the throat at the back of the nose. The adenoids are similar to the **tonsils**. They catch and destroy **bacteria** entering the body when a person breathes. They also help the body to build up a resistance, or **immunity**, to **infection**. Adenoids that become infected and swollen can make breathing difficult.
Adenoids can be removed by a simple operation.

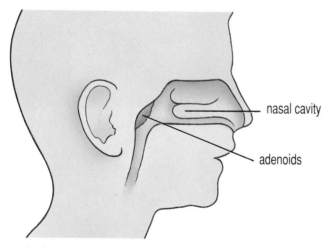

adolescence *noun*
Adolescence is the **age** between childhood and adulthood. A time of great physical and emotional change, it takes place, very approximately, from age 10 to age 20. At the beginning of adolescence, there is a period of rapid physical change and sexual development called **puberty**. Girls go through greater physical change than do boys, but adolescence is usually shorter for girls than for boys.
A boy's voice changes during adolescence and becomes deeper.

adrenal gland *noun*
The adrenal gland is a small **organ** that releases **hormones**. There are two adrenal glands, one on top of each **kidney**. The hormones they release, including **adrenalin**, help the body react to **stress** and allow the changes of **puberty** to begin.
The adrenal glands help to control the level of glucose in the bloodstream.

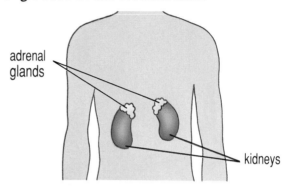

adrenalin *noun*
Adrenalin is a **hormone** produced by the **adrenal glands**. Adrenalin increases **heartbeat** and **respiration** in response to **stress**.
Adrenalin prepares the body for danger.

adult *noun*
An adult is a person who is fully grown and **mature**. Adults are sexually developed and can **reproduce**. People are adults once they have been through **adolescence**.
People spend the longest part of their life as an adult.

age *noun*
Age is a stage in a person's life. Childhood, **adolescence** and adulthood are all ages.
Old age is the last stage in a person's life.

aging *noun*
Aging is the process of becoming older. People grow during childhood and adolescence. Then they start gradually to age and their body slowly breaks down. A healthy **lifestyle** and medical care can slow down aging, and many people now live to be more than 80 years old.
Aging can cause the joints to become stiff.

AIDS *noun*
AIDS is a disease that breaks down the **immune system**, which is the body's defense against illness. AIDS stands for Acquired Immune Deficiency Syndrome and is caused by a **virus** called **HIV**. A person may have HIV in his or her body for many years before the actual disease of AIDS develops. AIDS is passed from person to person in bodily fluids such as **blood**.
There is no known cure for AIDS.

albino *adjective*
Albino describes someone who is born without any coloring in his or her skin, hair or eyes. Coloring is usually caused by **melanin**, a brown pigment. An albino person's eyes are clear and may look pink because the **blood vessels** show through.
The albino child had pure white hair.
albinism *noun*

alimentary canal *noun*
The alimentary canal is the tubes and organs inside the body that run from the **mouth** to the **rectum**. It includes the **esophagus**, **stomach**, and **intestines**. Food is taken into the body through the mouth and passes along the alimentary canal to the **anus**.
The mouth is the top opening of the alimentary canal.

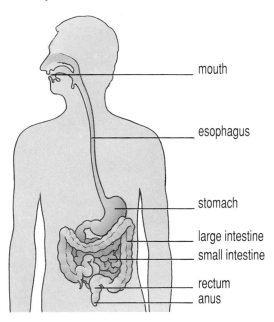

mouth
esophagus
stomach
large intestine
small intestine
rectum
anus

allergen *noun*
An allergen is a substance that causes an **allergy**.
Grass, cat fur, and house dust are allergens.

allergy *noun*
An allergy is an unusual reaction to a substance. A substance that causes an allergic reaction is called an **allergen**. If a person with an allergy comes in contact with an allergen, he or she may develop a skin rash, a runny nose, or itching eyes. **Hay fever** is an allergy to pollen.
The boy has an allergy to cow's milk.
allergic *adjective*

alternative medicine *noun*
Alternative medicine uses treatments that do not rely on **drugs** and **surgery**. People who practice alternative medicine try to treat the whole patient, using natural substances such as herbs, as well as techniques such as acupressure and mineral baths.
Acupuncture and osteopathy are examples of alternative medicine.

alveoli *noun*
Alveoli are the millions of tiny sacs at the end of the air passages in the lungs. The alveoli are surrounded by tiny blood vessels called **capillaries**. Oxygen in the air is breathed in during **respiration** and passes through the alveoli into the capillaries. Carbon dioxide passes from the **bloodstream** into the alveoli and is then breathed out.
The alveoli are part of the respiratory system.

Alzheimer's disease *noun*
Alzheimer's disease is a disorder of the **brain** that affects some people from the age of about 40 on. People with Alzheimer's disease suffer from loss of memory and from confusion. They eventually become unable to look after themselves. There is no treatment and no cure for Alzheimer's disease.
Some scientists believe that Alzheimer's disease is genetic and can be passed on by parents to their children.

amino acid *noun*
An amino acid is a substance found in **proteins**. There are about 20 amino acids in the human body, which combine in different ways to make all the proteins needed. The human body can make about 10 of these amino acids. The other 10 are found in foods, such as meat, fish, and certain vegetables.
Amino acids are an essential part of a person's diet.

amnesia *noun*
Amnesia is a loss of **memory**. A person might lose all his or her memory or may only lose memory for certain events. Amnesia may occur after a disease or an injury to the **head**. It can also occur as a reaction to an emotional upset.
She suffered amnesia after the automobile accident.

amniotic fluid *noun*
Amniotic fluid is the fluid inside the **uterus** of a pregnant woman. The **fetus** floats in the uterus, surrounded and protected by amniotic fluid.
Amniotic fluid lies inside the amniotic sac.

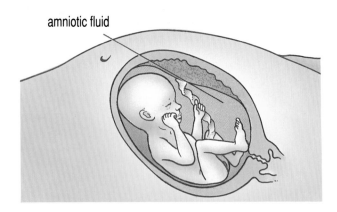

amniotic fluid

analgesic *noun*
An analgesic is a **drug** that relieves pain, without making a person **unconscious**. A person with a **headache** might take a type of analgesic called aspirin.
The doctor prescribed a strong analgesic to ease the patient's aching back.

anatomy ► page 10

anemia *noun*
Anemia is a disorder of the **blood** that results when the blood has less **hemoglobin** than it should. Anemia may result from a loss of blood after an accident or if the body cannot make enough red blood cells. People with anemia sometimes look pale and feel tired.
The woman with anemia was treated with iron tablets.

anesthesia *noun*
Anesthesia is the loss of feeling in all or part of the body. It can be produced by **drugs**, called **anesthetics**. Two forms of alternative medicine, hypnosis and **acupuncture**, can be used to cause anesthesia. It can also sometimes occur as a result of disease or injury, especially to the **nervous system**.
The boy needed anesthesia while his broken leg was set.

anesthetic *noun*
An anesthetic is a **drug** that causes a loss of feeling in the body. This is known as **anesthesia**. There are two main kinds of anesthetic. General anesthetics are used during surgical **operations** to make the patient **unconscious** and unable to feel any pain. Local anesthetics cause a loss of feeling in only part of the body, without making the patient unconscious.
The dentist gave her a local anesthetic before pulling out the tooth.

anger ► feelings

angina *noun*
Angina usually describes **spasms** of **pain** that people feel in their chest when too little oxygen reaches the **heart**. This can happen when the **blood vessels** leading to the heart muscle, called the **coronary arteries**, become partly blocked with fatty material carried in the blood.
Angina can be a warning of more serious heart disease.

8

ankle *noun*
The ankle is a part of the body that lies between the leg and the foot. It is made up of two bony lumps, one on either side of the leg. These are the ends of the two lower leg bones, called the **tibia** and the **fibula**. The **Achilles' tendon** lies at the back of the ankle. It helps to move the ankle **joint**.
The ice skater's strong ankles helped her to perform daring leaps and turns.

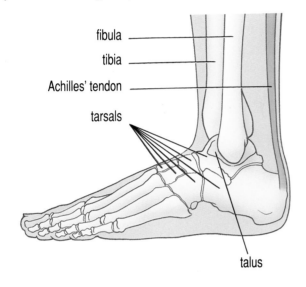

fibula
tibia
Achilles' tendon
tarsals
talus

anorexia *noun*
Anorexia is a loss of **appetite**. A person with anorexia does not want to eat anything. Anorexia nervosa is an emotional illness suffered mostly by **adolescent** girls and young women, who refuse to eat and suffer a very severe loss of weight.
She was very thin because she was suffering from anorexia.

anterior *adjective*
Anterior describes the parts of the human body that face forward. The opposite of anterior is **posterior**.
The chest is an anterior part of the body.

anti- *prefix*
Anti- is a prefix meaning against or preventing.
The traveler took anti-malaria tablets to protect him from the disease.

antibiotic *noun*
An antibiotic is a kind of **drug** that fights **bacteria** in the human body. Scientists have developed many kinds of antibiotics to fight the different bacteria that cause **diseases**. Some antibiotics are made from natural substances, such as fungi or molds; **penicillin** is one of these. Other antibiotics are made from synthetic materials.
A course of antibiotics cured his throat infection.

antibody *noun*
An antibody is a part of the body's defense, or **immune system**. When **bacteria** or **viruses** enter the body, they produce substances called **antigens**. Special **white blood** cells called lymphocytes react to the presence of antigens and make antibodies, which attack and kill the invading bacteria or viruses.
Antibodies help a person to fight infection.

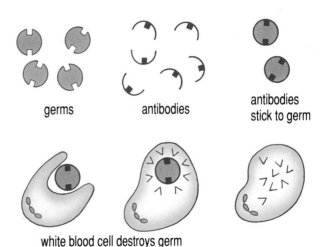

germs   antibodies   antibodies stick to germ

white blood cell destroys germ

antidote *noun*
An antidote is a substance that fights the harmful effects of poison in the body. Most poisons have only one kind of antidote. If the wrong kind of antidote is used with a poison, it may make the effects of the poison worse.
When he was bitten by a poisonous snake, the antidote stopped the farmer from becoming seriously ill.

anatomy *noun*

Anatomy is the study of how the body is put together. It involves looking at the different parts of the body, and grouping them together in a **system**. For example, the anatomy of the digestive system includes all the parts of the body concerned with digestion.

She cut open the heart to study its anatomy.

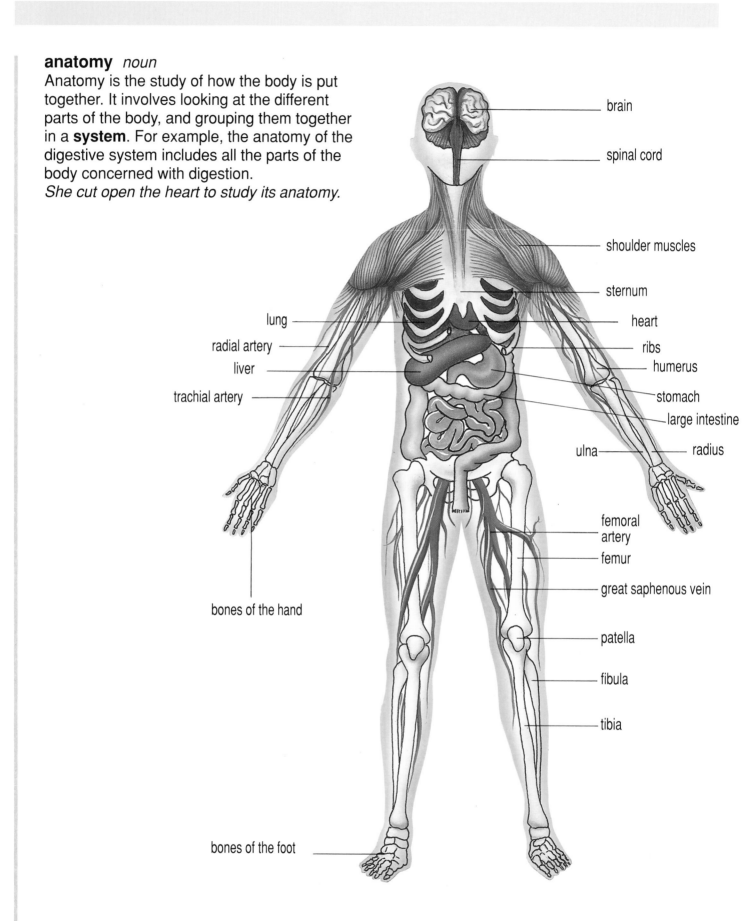

brain

spinal cord

shoulder muscles

sternum

heart

ribs

humerus

stomach

large intestine

radius

lung

radial artery

liver

trachial artery

ulna

femoral artery

femur

great saphenous vein

patella

fibula

tibia

bones of the hand

bones of the foot

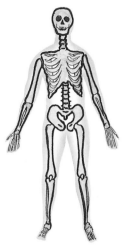

The skeletal system includes the body's framework of bones.

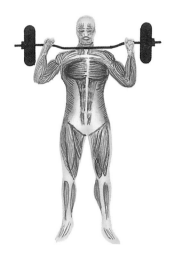

The muscular system includes all the muscles that help the body move.

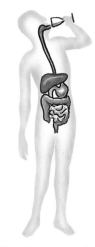

The digestive system involves all the parts of the body that process food.

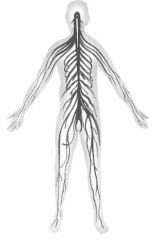

The nervous system connects nerve cells in the body with the brain.

The respiratory system consists of the lungs, nose, and air passages.

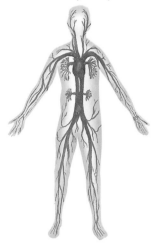

The circulatory system includes the heart and all the blood vessels.

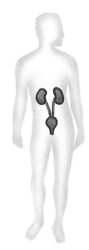

The kidneys, ureters and bladder make up the urinary system.

The endocrine system consists of glands which produce hormones.

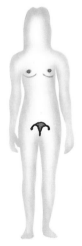

The reproductive system includes all the organs to do with sex.

antigen *noun*
An antigen is a kind of **protein** that is made when **germs**, such as **bacteria** and **viruses**, have found their way inside the human body. Special **blood cells** notice the antigens in the bloodstream, go into action, and produce **antibodies** to fight and kill the germs.
Antigens warn the body's defense system that germs have invaded the body.

antiseptic *noun*
An antiseptic is a substance that is put on skin and mucous membrane to help stop **infection**. It kills **germs** and prevents them from spreading. **Disinfectants** are used to kill germs on nonliving things.
She put antiseptic on the cut to stop it from becoming infected.

antitoxin *noun*
An antitoxin is a kind of **antibody** that is part of the body's defense, or **immune system**. Antitoxins are made by the **blood** to protect it from a poison, or **toxin**, that has entered the body.
Antitoxins fight the poisons produced by some bacteria.

anus *noun*
The anus is an opening in the body. It lies at the end of the **rectum** and is the final part of the **alimentary canal**. Solid waste material is produced during the **digestion** of food and passes out of the body through the anus. The **sphincter** muscle opens and closes the anus.
The anus is the lower opening of the digestive system.
anal *adjective*

anvil *noun*
The anvil is one of three tiny bones inside the **ear**, which are known as the **ossicles**. The anvil joins the **hammer** to the **stirrup**. The three bones carry sound vibrations from the **eardrum** to the **inner ear**.
The anvil is a bone that passes on sound in the process of hearing.

anxiety ▶ **feelings**

aorta *noun*
The aorta is the largest **artery** in the body. **Blood** flows through the aorta from the **heart**, then joins with other arteries which take the blood to all parts of the body.
The aorta carries blood from the heart to the rest of the body.

appendicitis *noun*
Appendicitis is an **infection** of a part of the body called the **appendix**. The infection is caused by **bacteria** and makes the appendix become inflamed. It swells up and fills with **pus**. A person with appendicitis feels pain in the lower right-hand corner of the **abdomen**, and has a slight fever. Usually, the infected appendix has to be removed in an emergency operation called an appendectomy.
The boy's appendicitis was cured when the surgeon took his appendix out.

appendix *noun*
The appendix is a part of the body joined to the first part of the **large intestine**, called the **cecum**. It is worm-shaped and about 3–4 inches long. The appendix can become infected and cause **appendicitis**.
The appendix lies in the lower right side of the abdomen.

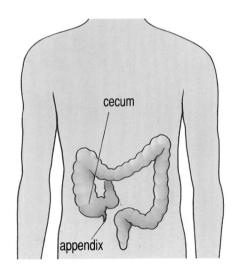

appetite *noun*
Appetite is the natural, healthy desire for food. People may lose their appetite when they are ill. Some strong, unpleasant **feelings**, such as anxiety, can cause a loss of appetite.
He had such a good appetite that he ate three eggs for breakfast.

arm *noun*
An arm is one of the upper **limbs** of the body. It is made up of the upper arm, the **elbow**, and the forearm. The arm is joined to the body at the **shoulder** and to the **hand** at the **wrist**. The upper arm bone is called the **humerus**. The two forearm bones are the **radius** and the **ulna**. **Muscles** attached to the bones help the arm to move.
The father held the sleeping baby with his left arm as he fed her.

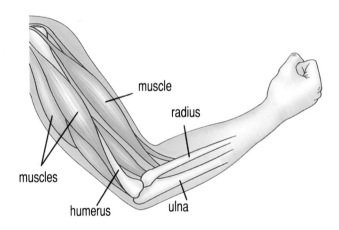

artery *noun*
An artery is a flexible tube inside the body, with thick, strong walls. Arteries carry blood mixed with oxygen from the **heart** to all parts of the body. Tiny **muscles** in the artery walls help the heart to push the blood along. This flow of blood along the arteries can be felt as the **pulse**. The walls of arteries may become thicker and harder, and narrowed by fat deposits. This makes it more difficult for blood to flow through and can cause **heart disease**.
The carotid arteries lie in the neck.

arthritis *noun*
Arthritis is a disorder of the **joints**, in which they become painful, stiff, and swollen. It may be caused by **inflammation** or **infection** in the joint. Sometimes arthritis is a **symptom** of another **disease**. Some people have arthritis in old age when their joints begin wearing out. There is no cure for arthritis, but **drugs** can help to ease the pain and inflammation.
With some kinds of arthritis, diseased joints can be replaced with artificial ones.

artificial *adjective*
Artificial describes something that is made by people and is not natural. A person who has lost a leg, for example, could have an artificial **limb** fitted. Artificial **respiration** is used to save the life of a person who has stopped breathing. It forces air into the lungs and helps the person to start breathing again naturally.
The lifeguards learned how to perform artificial respiration.

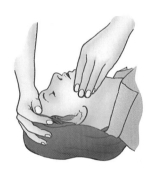

asthma noun
Asthma is a breathing disorder that occurs when small tubes in the **lungs** become narrowed. This makes it difficult for a person to breathe. The chest feels tight, and the person makes a wheezing sound. Asthma is usually caused by an **allergy**. **Infection**, cold weather, tiredness, or **stress** can also bring on asthma. **Drugs** can help people who suffer from asthma attacks.
His asthma attack was relieved by using an inhaler.

astigmatism *noun*
Astigmatism is a disorder of the **eye** that results in blurred, or distorted, **sight**. It is caused if the outer layer of the eye, called the **cornea**, curves the wrong way. It also occurs if the part of the eye called the **lens** is slightly out of shape. If it is serious, astigmatism can be corrected by wearing eyeglasses.
Almost everyone has a small amount of astigmatism.

athlete's foot *noun*
Athlete's foot is a skin infection which often occurs between the **toes**. It is caused by one of two kinds of **fungus**. The skin becomes blistered, sore, and itchy. If the **blisters** break, **bacteria** may enter the skin and cause another infection. Athlete's foot can be treated with lotions, ointments, or powders bought at a **pharmacy** or drugstore.
His sister caught athlete's foot at the swimming pool.

atlas *noun*
The atlas is a ring-shaped **bone**. It is the part of the **spine** that supports the **skull**. The atlas is the first of the bones in the neck, or **cervical vertebrae**.
The atlas is joined to a vertebra called the axis.

atrium (plural **atria**) *noun*
An atrium (also called an auricle) is a hollow space, or **cavity**. It is used to refer to the two upper chambers in the **heart** where blood is collected during **circulation**. They are called the left atrium and the right atrium. From the atria, the blood flows to the **ventricles**, where it is pumped to the arteries.
The right atrium receives blood from the body and the left atrium receives blood from the lungs.

audible *adjective*
Audible describes a sound that can be heard.
The explosion was audible from a great distance.

auditory *adjective*
Auditory describes anything to do with **hearing**. The auditory **nerve** is the main nerve of the **inner ear**. The auditory range is the total number of sounds that a person can hear.
One's auditory abilities usually weaken as one ages.

aural *adjective*
Aural describes anything to do with the **ear**. Aural **surgery** involves operations on the ear.
The doctor used an aural instrument to examine her ear.

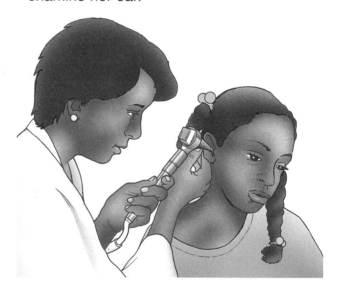

auricle ► **atrium**

autism *noun*
Autism is a rare disorder of the **mind** that usually appears in early childhood. Children with autism are unable to relate to other people. They often cannot speak, and may injure themselves on purpose. Children with autism may be mentally handicapped, but they are physically normal. It is not known what causes autism. The **symptoms** can be treated with a kind of teaching, or with behavior modification.
Autism affects boys more often than girls, and it cannot be cured.
autistic *adjective*

axilla (plural **axillae**) *noun*
Axilla is the scientific term for an armpit. It is a hollow, or **cavity**, below the shoulder joint. Strong **muscles** make up the front and back walls of the axillae. These muscles are attached to the chest and shoulder blade and help to move the **arms**.
An axilla contains sweat glands and lymph glands.
axillary adjective

axis *noun*
The axis is a ring-shaped **bone**. A part of the **spine**, the axis is the second of the bones in the neck, called the **cervical vertebrae**.
The axis is one of seven bones in the neck.

baby *noun*
A baby is a human child, from birth to the age of about two years. Unlike the young of some other mammals, human babies are completely helpless at birth.
The baby was just beginning to walk at the age of eleven months.

back *noun*
The back is the part of the human body between the **neck** and the **pelvis**. It is a **posterior** part, which means it faces backward. The back includes the **spine**, **shoulders**, shoulder blades, and **ribs**.
The walker carried a rucksack on his back.

backache *noun*
Backache is a very common kind of **pain** and can be felt in any part of the area around the **spine**. Backache has many different causes. The most common ones are strained **muscles** or **ligaments**, and disorders of the **bones** or **nerves** in the back. Certain drugs, called **analgesics**, can ease the pain of backache. Physiotherapy is a useful kind of treatment for severe backache.
He had a backache after lifting the heavy boxes.

backbone ► spine

bacteria (singular **bacterium**) *plural noun*
Bacteria are microorganisms and a kind of
germ. Most bacteria are harmless, and some
kinds, such as those found in our **intestines**,
are essential to life. However, some types of
bacteria can cause **diseases** in the body.
*Bacteria in the drinking water made the
people at the campsite ill.*

balance *noun*
Balance is the ability to stand or move
upright and not fall over. It is controlled by
the part of the brain called the **cerebellum**,
which is helped by the **inner ear**. When the
position of the body changes, the cerebellum
sends messages to the **muscles** telling them
to keep the body in balance. Upset balance,
or **dizziness**, can be caused by travel
sickness, ear infections, or when not enough
blood and oxygen reach the brain.
*The boy found it hard to keep his balance the
first time he used a skateboard.*

ball and socket joint ► joint

behavior *noun*
Behavior is the way people act or react.
Some kinds of behavior, such as **breathing**,
do not have to be learned. They are
instinctive. Other kinds of behavior, such as
speaking, have to be learned.
*Smiling is a kind of behavior that babies
learn when they are a few weeks old.*

benign *adjective*
Benign describes something that is not life-
threatening. A benign **disease** is mild and
does not last long. A benign growth in the
body, or tumor, does not contain dangerous
cancer cells that could spread.
*She recovered quickly after the benign tumor
was removed.*

beriberi *noun*
Beriberi is a **disease** that is caused by a lack
of vitamin B1 in a person's **diet** over a long
period. Vitamin B1 is found in foods such as
wheat germ, liver, beans, and brown rice.
Beriberi affects the **muscles** in a person's
body, causing stiffness and pain. After a time,
it affects the **nervous system**, and the
person may become paralyzed. Beriberi is
treated with a series of vitamin B1
injections, and a diet rich in this vitamin.
*Beriberi used to be common in Asia when
white rice was sometimes the only food
available.*

biceps *noun*
The biceps is a **muscle**. In the upper **arm**,
the biceps is the muscle at the front. It works
together with the **triceps**, to bend the arm at
the **elbow**. In the **thigh**, the biceps femoris
lies at the back, and helps to bend the **knee**.
*The biceps is a flexor muscle, which means it
pulls the arm to bend at the elbow.*

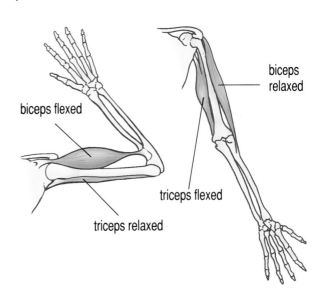

biceps relaxed

biceps flexed

triceps flexed

triceps relaxed

bile *noun*
Bile is a yellowish-green liquid that is made by the **liver**. Bile is made up of **cholesterol**, bile salts, **proteins**, and urea, which is also found in **urine**. Bile is stored in the **gall bladder**. It passes into the **intestine**, where it helps to break down, or **digest**, fats.
Bile gets its color from by a substance called bilirubin.
bilious *adjective*

bilharzia *noun*
Bilharzia is a disease caused by a worm that infects the **liver**, **kidneys**, **lungs**, and other **organs**. The worms that cause the disease live in water in tropical countries. A person with bilharzia has **fever**, **cough**, muscle pain, and irritation of the **skin**. There may also be internal bleeding. The disease is treated with a type of **drug**. Bilharzia is also known as schistosomiasis.
He caught bilharzia from swimming in an infected lake.

binocular vision ► sight

biological clock *noun*
Biological clock is a term that describes the way the body's activities are timed. It times the need to sleep and the need to wake up. The biological clock controls a person's body **temperature**, and tells him or her when to eat or drink. A person who travels by airplane across several time zones to a distant part of the world, will find that his or her biological clock is upset for a few days.
Her biological clock told her it was bedtime, although it was only 6 P.M.

biology *noun*
Biology is the study of living things. It looks at how plants and animals are made, how they develop and behave, and where they live. A person who studies biology is called a biologist.
He learned about the circulation of the blood in biology class.
biological *adjective*

biopsy *noun*
A biopsy is a kind of medical test. In a biopsy, a tiny piece of **tissue** is removed and examined under a microscope to see if there is any **disease**, such as cancer, present.
The surgeon performed a biopsy to find out whether the lump in her leg was malignant.

birth ► childbirth

bite *noun*
A bite is a wound on the **skin** made by an animal or an insect. Most bites are not dangerous. They only need to be kept clean, so they do not become infected. The bites of poisonous snakes and spiders inject **toxins** into the body that must be treated with special drugs called **antidotes**. Some insects and other animals carry **diseases**, such as **malaria**, which they pass on to people when they bite them.
The mosquito bites on her arm itched for a few days.

bladder *noun*
The bladder is a strong, muscular bag inside the body. It lies just behind the bone called the **pubis**. Liquid waste, called **urine**, is produced by the **kidneys** and stored in the bladder. When the bladder is full, it pushes the urine out of the body through a tube called the **urethra**.
The bladder of an adult can hold about half a quart of urine.

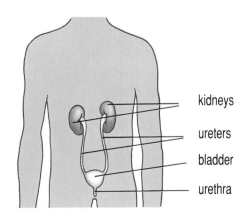

kidneys
ureters
bladder
urethra

bleed   *verb*
Bleed means to lose blood from any part of
the body. When the **skin** is cut, the wound
bleeds. Some kinds of injury or disease can
cause inner body parts to bleed. This is
called internal bleeding.
*His knee bled after he fell on the sharp
stones.*

blindness   *noun*
Blindness is the lack of **sight** in one or both
eyes. It may be present at birth, or it may
happen later on and occur either gradually or
suddenly. Blindness may occur as a result of
a disorder of the eye itself, such as
glaucoma or **cataracts**. It can also happen if
there is something wrong with the part of the
brain that controls sight.
*People suffering from blindness can learn to
read using a system of raised dots, called
Braille.*

blink   *verb*
Blink means to make rapid, up and down
movements of the **eyelids**. People blink their
eyelids every few seconds to keep their eyes
moistened with tears. They blink to protect
their eyes from very bright light or from
smoke in the air. People also blink as a
reflex action when an object suddenly
comes near their eyes.
*People blink their eyelids all the time without
thinking about it.*

blister   *noun*
A blister is a bump on the skin that contains
a clear, watery fluid called **serum**. Blisters
usually form when the skin is irritated,
rubbed, or pinched. A **burn** may also cause
a blister. A blood blister is caused by burst
blood vessels under the skin.
*She had a blister on her heel because her
shoes were too tight.*

blood ► page 20

blood cell   *noun*
There are three main kinds of blood cells.
Red blood cells carry **oxygen** to all parts of
the body. White blood cells help the body to
fight **infection** and **disease**. **Platelets** stop
leaks in blood vessels and help the blood to
clot.
Blood cells are also known as corpuscles.

blood count ► **blood test**

blood group   *noun*
Scientists have sorted human blood into
different blood groups. A person's blood
group depends on what kinds of **protein** are
present on his or her red **blood cells**. The
most common method of sorting blood is
called the ABO system. Under this system,
the blood groups are A, B, O, or AB. When a
person is given blood during a **transfusion**,
it is essential that this blood group is
compatible with his or her own.
The test showed that her blood group was B.

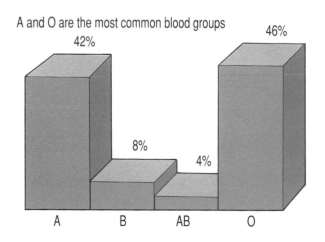

A and O are the most common blood groups

blood pressure *noun*
Blood pressure is the pressure of the blood against the walls of the **arteries**. The amount of blood pressure depends on how strongly and quickly the heart contracts and pushes the blood along the arteries. It also depends on how much blood is flowing and how elastic the artery walls are. Blood pressure can be measured with a special instrument. *High blood pressure can be a sign of heart disease.*

blood test *noun*
A blood test is really a series of tests that is done on a sample of **blood**. In a blood test, a small amount of blood is taken from the body and examined to see whether the person is in good health. A blood test usually includes a count of the different kinds of **blood cells**. *The blood test showed she had a low count of red blood cells and was anemic.*

blood vessel *noun*
A blood vessel is a tube in the body through which blood flows, or **circulates**. The main blood vessels are the **arteries**, **veins**, and **capillaries**.
The smallest blood vessels are the capillaries.

bloodstream *noun*
The bloodstream is the **blood** flowing around the body in the **blood vessels**. The **heart** pumps the blood around the body.
Oxygen enters the bloodstream in the lungs and is carried around the body.

blushing *noun*
Blushing is a sudden reddening of the skin of the face and neck. It happens when the tiny **blood vessels** near the surface of the skin become more open, or dilated. Extra blood rushes into the dilated vessels, and makes the skin look red. Blushing may happen if a person becomes hot, or if he or she feels an emotion such as anger or excitement.
Blushing is most often linked to a feeling of embarrassment.

body temperature ► temperature

boil *noun*
A boil is a skin disorder. It is an **infection** of a hair root or of a **sweat gland**, caused by **bacteria**. A boil begins as a red, painful lump on the skin. It grows bigger, and after about three days a yellow head forms. The boil must burst and let out **pus** before it can heal. **Antibiotics** are sometimes used to treat boils.
Boils may come back if the skin is not kept clean.

bone *noun*
Bone is the hard, stiff substance that makes up the body's framework, or **skeleton**. It supports the body, and protects the delicate inner **organs**. Bone is mostly made up of **calcium** salts, held together with strong fibers. It is usually hollow, and bone **marrow** and **minerals** are stored inside. There are two kinds of bone. **Compact bone** is hard and solid. **Cancellous bone** looks spongy. Humans have about 200 long and short bones.
The child's broken arm bone mended quickly.

bone marrow *noun*
Bone marrow is a kind of soft tissue that is found in the hollow center of **bones**. Red bone marrow has special **cells** that make fresh **blood** for the body. Yellow bone marrow is mostly **fat**.
Bone marrow produces over 100 million red blood cells every minute.

blood *noun*

Blood is a red fluid that continually flows through the **blood vessels**. Blood is pumped round the body by the **heart**. The blood transports food and oxygen to all living **cells** in the body, and takes away waste matter from them.

An adult male has about 12 pints of blood in his body.

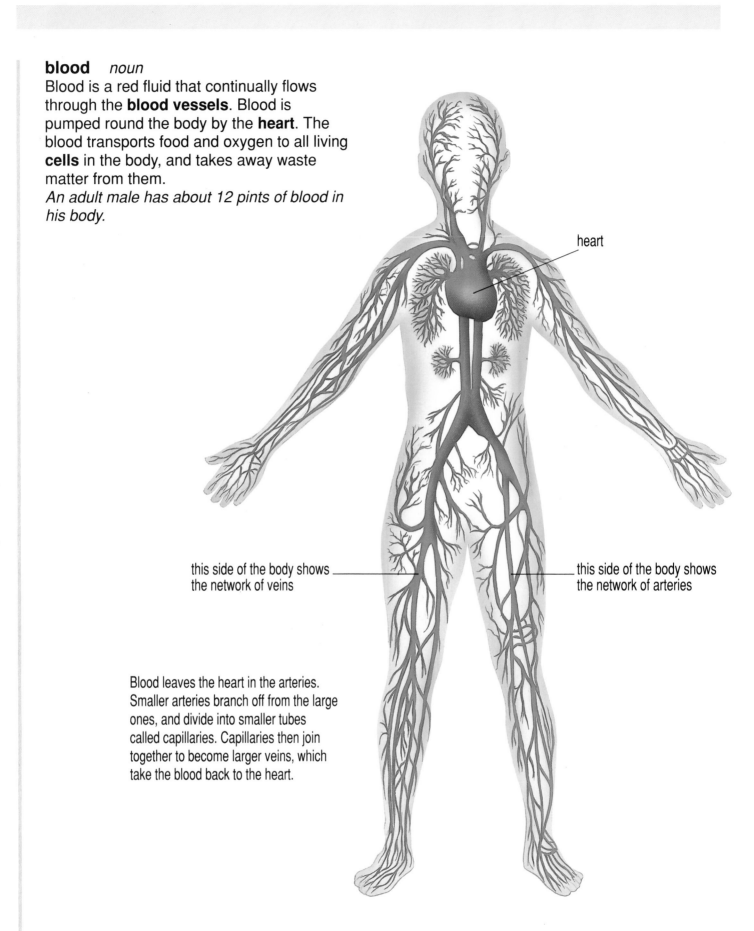

heart

this side of the body shows the network of veins

this side of the body shows the network of arteries

Blood leaves the heart in the arteries. Smaller arteries branch off from the large ones, and divide into smaller tubes called capillaries. Capillaries then join together to become larger veins, which take the blood back to the heart.

Blood consists mainly of a watery liquid called plasma. Floating in the plasma are red cells, white cells, and platelets. The disk-shaped red blood cells take oxygen from the lungs to the tissues. White blood cells are larger than red blood cells and there are 500 red cells to every white one. White blood cells help to fight infection by attacking harmful bacteria. Small particles called platelets are important in blood clotting.

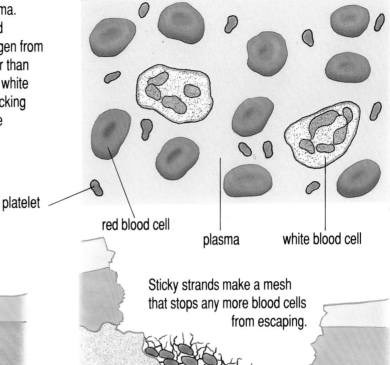

platelet

red blood cell

plasma

white blood cell

When a blood vessel is cut, platelets rush to the wound and form a kind of plug.

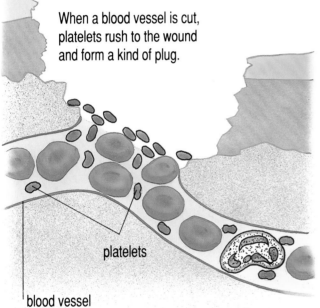

platelets

blood vessel

Sticky strands make a mesh that stops any more blood cells from escaping.

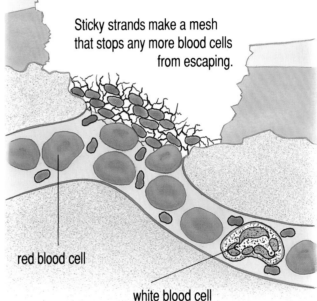

red blood cell

white blood cell

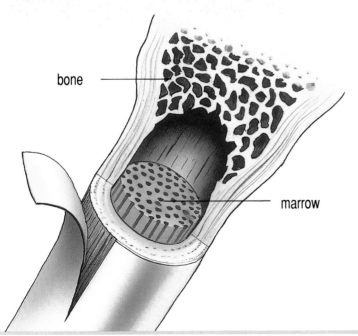

bone

marrow

Blood is made in the bone marrow. A red blood cell lives for about 120 days after it enters the bloodstream. When blood cells die, they are disposed of by the liver and the spleen. The bone marrow continuously makes new blood cells to replace dead cells.

botulism *noun*
Botulism is a rare kind of food poisoning that attacks the **nervous system**. The **toxin** that causes botulism is usually found in foods that have not been properly prepared for canning or preserving. The first symptoms include general weakness, blurred vision, **nausea**, and **diarrhea**. Botulism needs immediate treatment with **antitoxins**, as it develops very quickly and is often fatal.
Modern methods of canning food have made botulism very rare.

bowel ► **intestine**

brain ► page 24

brain stem *noun*
The brain stem is the stalk-like base of the **brain** that joins the **cerebrum** to the **spinal cord**. The brain stem controls the **involuntary systems**, such as breathing, heartbeat, and blood circulation.
Your brain stem keeps your heart beating regularly.

breast *noun*
The breast is on the front of the chest. In **adolescent** girls and women, the breasts are the **mammary glands**. Girls begin to grow breasts at **puberty**. When fully grown, each breast contains 15 to 20 milk glands that produce milk after **childbirth**. Each of these glands has a tube, or **duct**, that leads to the **nipple**. The rest of the breast is fatty **tissue**.
The baby drank milk from his mother's breast.

breast-feeding *noun*
Breast-feeding is the act of feeding a **baby** at the **breast**. During the first two or three days of breast-feeding, the breasts produce a substance called **colostrum**. Three to five days after **childbirth**, milk begins to flow. Breast milk is easy to **digest**, and protects the baby against **allergies** and **disease**.
Breast-feeding helps the mother to form a close bond with her baby.

breathing ► **respiration**

breathing rate *noun*
The breathing rate is the speed at which air is drawn into and let out of the **lungs**. It varies according to how active or still a person is. The more active a person is, the faster his or her breathing rate becomes.
The sleeping child's breathing rate was slow and even.

bronchial *adjective*
Bronchial describes anything to do with the air passages called the **bronchi**. A bronchial dilator, or bronchodilator, is a kind of drug which widens the airways to the lungs to help people with breathing difficulties.
Bronchial disorders affect the lungs and can cause breathing problems.

bronchial dilator

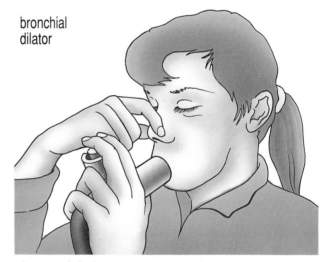

bronchiole *noun*
A bronchiole is a tiny tube in the **lung**. As the windpipe, or **trachea**, reaches the lungs, it branches into two **bronchi**. In turn, the bronchi branch into tiny 'twigs' called bronchioles. A bronchiole is about half a millimeter in diameter and lined with smooth **muscle**. Air passes through the bronchioles into the **alveoli**, which are the tiny sacs found in the lungs. Then the air passes through the bronchioles again, to be breathed out.
There are more than 250,000 bronchioles in a person's lungs.

bronchitis   *noun*
Bronchitis is **inflammation** of the **bronchi**.
Acute bronchitis begins suddenly and can
end after treatment with antibiotics. It may
follow a nose or throat infection. **Chronic**
bronchitis develops slowly, and is more
difficult to treat.
*Her bronchitis improved when she stopped
smoking.*

broncho-   *prefix*
Broncho- is a prefix meaning to do with the
bronchi. Bronchopneumonia is a kind of
pneumonia that affects the bronchi.
*The doctor used a bronchoscope to inspect
her bronchi.*

bronchoscope   *noun*
A bronchoscope is a kind of medical
instrument. It is a long, thin tube, with a light
on the end. Doctors use bronchoscopes to
look down a patient's **trachea** and **bronchi**.
They can also be used for removing objects
that have been breathed in accidentally.
*He looked down the bronchoscope and saw
a button in the little boy's windpipe.*

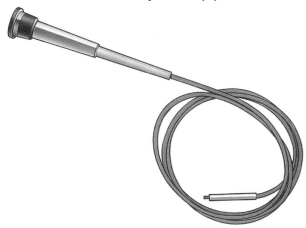

bronchus (plural **bronchi**)   *noun*
The bronchi are two tubes that branch off
from the **trachea**. One bronchus goes to
each **lung**. The bronchi carry air to and from
the lungs, during the process of **respiration**.
They are lined with special **cells** that act like
hairs, sweeping **mucus** and dust away from
the lungs and toward the throat.
Bronchitis is inflammation of the bronchi.

bruise   *noun*
A bruise is a minor injury caused by a blow to
the body, or a fall. It appears beneath the
skin as a purplish mark. The color of a bruise
is caused by blood escaping from tiny **blood
vessels** that are broken by the sudden
pressure on the skin. The color fades
gradually, changing to blue, then brown, then
yellow, before it disappears. A bruise may be
painful and swollen.
*The pain and swelling of a bruise can be
reduced by applying an ice pack.*

bulimia   *noun*
Bulimia is an eating disorder. People with
bulimia have frequent periods of overeating,
called binges, which they cannot control.
After each food binge, they usually make
themselves **vomit** so that they will not gain
weight. Bulimia is an emotional illness that is
often connected to **anorexia** nervosa.
*Bulimia may be treated with psychotherapy,
or antidepressant drugs.*

bunion   *noun*
A bunion is a hard swelling on the big toe
joint at the side of the foot. The tissues over
the swelling become red, inflamed and often
painful. A bunion is made worse by tight-
fitting shoes. The disorder is often
hereditary, which means it is passed on in
families. If a bunion becomes very severe, it
can be removed by an **operation**.
*Wearing loose shoes helped to ease the
discomfort of his bunion.*

brain *noun*

The brain is an **organ** in the body. It is the control center of the body's **nervous system.** The brain sends out and receives hundreds of messages every second. It controls every activity of the body, such as moving the **muscles** and **breathing**. It also controls all the functions of the **mind**, such as **thinking** and remembering. The brain is made up of soft tissue which is protected by the hard bones of the **skull.**

Some part of the brain controls every function of the body.

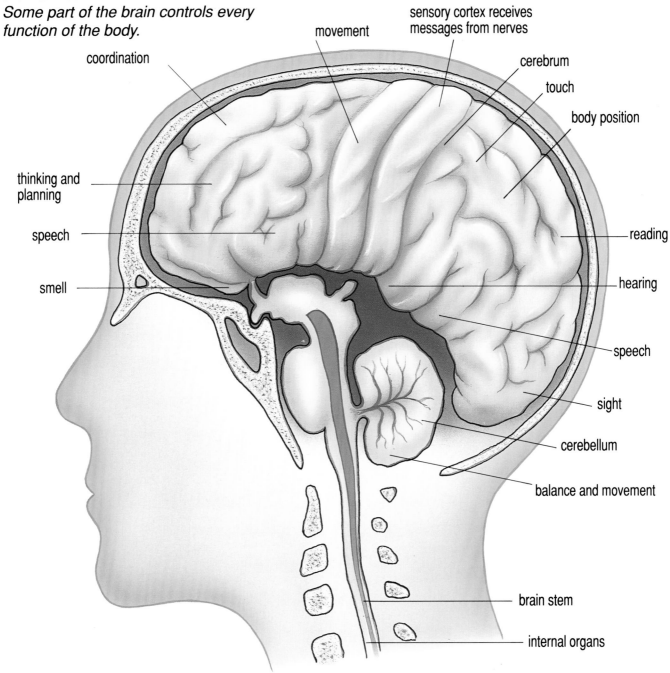

coordination

movement

sensory cortex receives messages from nerves

cerebrum

touch

body position

thinking and planning

speech

smell

reading

hearing

speech

sight

cerebellum

balance and movement

brain stem

internal organs

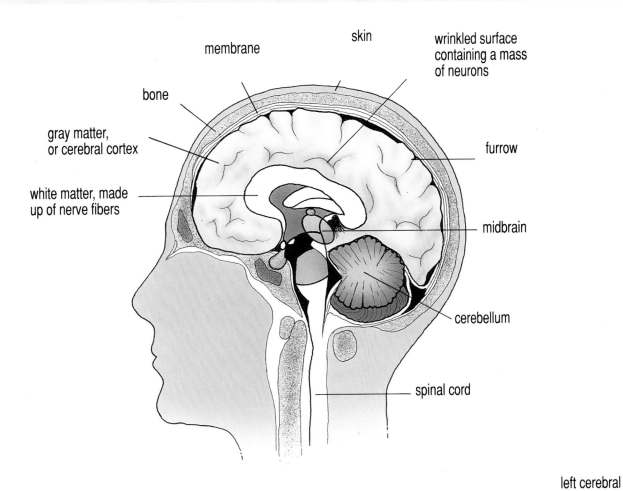

membrane

skin

wrinkled surface containing a mass of neurons

bone

gray matter, or cerebral cortex

furrow

white matter, made up of nerve fibers

midbrain

cerebellum

spinal cord

Messages travel up nerve pathways to the thalamus, which coordinates messages to and from the brain. As they go, the pathways cross from one side to the other. So the left cerebral hemisphere is linked with the right side of the body, and the right cerebral hemisphere controls the left side of the body. The pathways from the two sides of the cerebellum also cross over.

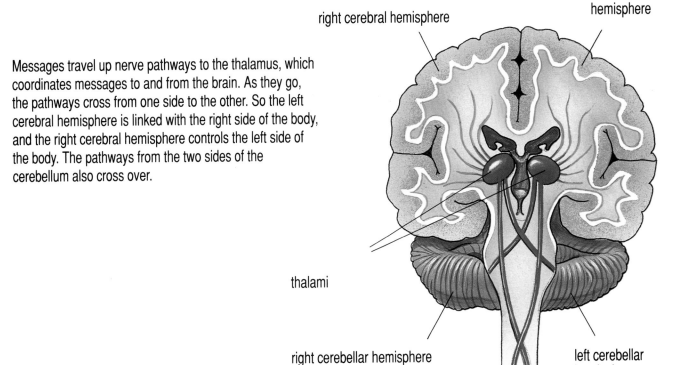

right cerebral hemisphere

left cerebral hemisphere

thalami

right cerebellar hemisphere

left cerebellar hemisphere

burn *noun*

A burn is damage to the **skin** caused by heat, cold, radiation, or certain chemicals. Burns are grouped according to how deep they are. First-degree burns produce a patch of red skin and heal without forming a **scar**. Second-degree burns go deeper and cause the skin to blister. Third-degree burns destroy the skin and the **tissues** underneath, such as fat or muscle. They leave an open area, and a skin **graft** is needed to prevent serious scarring. People with large, deep burns require emergency medical help.
Sunburn is an example of a first-degree burn.

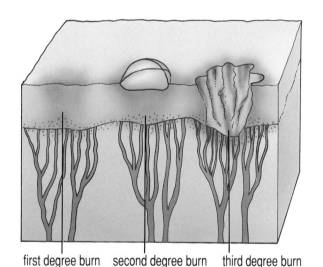

first degree burn   second degree burn   third degree burn

calcaneus ► heel

calcium *noun*

Calcium is a mineral that the body needs to maintain good health. It helps muscles to contract, and it also helps blood to clot properly. Too little calcium in a body can lead to bone diseases, such as **rickets**. Calcium is found in foods such as milk and cheese.
Milk and milk products, such as cheese and yogurt, are all good sources of calcium.

calorie *noun*

Calories measure the **energy** value of food. Some foods, such as fats, contain many calories, while others, such as vegetables, contain few calories. The amount of calories a person needs each day depends on his or her age, sex, build, and level of activity. A person who takes in too many calories will put on weight.
She reduced her calorie intake to lose weight.

canal *noun*

A canal is a tube that carries food, liquid, or air from one part of the body to another.
A baby is born through the birth canal.

cancer *noun*

Cancer is a **disease** in which **cells** grow without control in a way that can destroy healthy **tissue** and endanger life. Cancers can occur in any part of the body. Many kinds can be completely cured, but cancer remains a major cause of death.
Many people try to avoid substances, such as tobacco smoke, that can cause cancer.

canine ▶ tooth

capillary *noun*
A capillary is the smallest type of **blood vessel**. Capillaries connect the smallest **arteries** with the smallest **veins**. They can be so tiny that only one blood cell at a time is able to pass along them. Capillaries carry blood rich in **oxygen** to the tissues, and carry away **waste** products.
There are capillaries in all parts of the body.

carbohydrate *noun*
A carbohydrate is a type of food and an essential source of energy for the body. Carbohydrates should be eaten as part of a balanced diet. Eating too few carbohydrates can cause **fatigue** and depression, while eating too many can lead to obesity and **heart disease**. All sugars and starches are carbohydrates. Foods with a high carbohydrate content include potatoes, bananas, cereals, and bread.
Whole grains are a good source of carbohydrates.

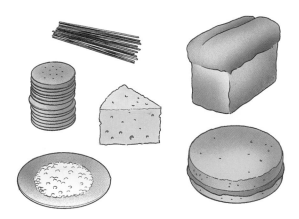

carbon dioxide *noun*
Carbon dioxide is a colorless and odorless gas. Carbon dioxide is produced in body **tissues** as a **waste** product. It dissolves in **blood**, and is carried by the blood to the **lungs**. Here it is passed in the **alveoli**, and is breathed out of the body.
People and other animals give off carbon dioxide in the process of respiration.

carcinogen *noun*
A carcinogen is any substance known to cause **cancer**. Tobacco and asbestos are both carcinogens.
The scientists discovered that the substance was a carcinogen and warned people not to use it.

carcinoma *noun*
A carcinoma is a type of cancer. Carcinomas form in the layers of tissue that make up the inside and the outside of most **organs** of the body. The most common carcinomas occur in the skin, stomach, lungs, prostate gland, and breast. The growths are **malignant**, and can spread to other parts of the body. Carcinomas are usually treated by being surgically removed.
The surgeon successfully removed the carcinoma from the man's stomach.

cardiac *adjective*
Cardiac describes anything to do with the heart. Cardiac arrest is the sudden stopping of the heart.
Cardiac muscle is the medical name for the heart muscle.

cardiovascular system *noun*
The cardiovascular system, which includes the **heart** and the **blood vessels**, circulates **blood** throughout the body. Blood is pumped by the heart through the **arteries** to **capillaries** and **veins**. The blood takes food and oxygen to every living cell, and carries away waste products. There are about 35,000 miles of tubes in the adult cardiovascular system, and about 12 pints of blood.
The heart pumps blood around the cardiovascular system.

caries *noun*
Caries is the decaying of bone, especially teeth. Caries often involves **inflammation** of the surrounding soft **tissue**.
Caries had made a cavity in his tooth, which the dentist filled.

27

carotid artery ▶ **artery**

cartilage *noun*
Cartilage is very strong **connective tissue**. It has a whitish color, or it is semi-transparent. Part of the **nose** is formed from cartilage, and so are some **ribs**. Cartilage is also found between some of the **vertebrae** of the spine, and as a covering on the surface of **joints**. Cartilage can withstand heavy wear and tear.
He tore the cartilage in his knee, and suffered great pain.

cataract *noun*
A cataract is a nontransparent, or opaque, area in the **lens** of the **eye** that causes a person to gradually lose his or her sight. Injury to the fetus may cause it to be born with cataracts. Cataracts may also form after injury to the eye or in later life. They may be a symptom of diseases such as **diabetes**. Cataracts are quite painless and can be removed by surgery.
The old woman had her cataracts removed and replaced with artificial lenses.

catarrh *noun*
Catarrh is a mucous discharge from the upper airway. It is a symptom of various **infections**, such as colds and hay fever. The **mucous membranes** lining the nose and throat can become inflamed, producing large amounts of **mucus**.
He always suffered from catarrh when he caught a cold.

cauterize *verb*
To cauterize is to destroy tissue on purpose by burning it. A doctor may use heat, cold, electricity, or lasers, to cauterize. Wounds that are likely to become infected can be cauterized, and so can some scar tissue. Surgeons sometimes cauterize small blood vessels to stop them from bleeding during operations.
He cauterized the wound to prevent it from becoming infected.
cautery *noun*

cavity *noun*
A cavity is an enclosed space inside the body. It may be a large space, such as the abdominal cavity, or it may be a small hole in a tooth caused by decay, or **caries**.
The oral cavity is the space inside the mouth.

cecum *noun*
The cecum is the first part of the **large intestine**. It is found just beyond the point where the lower part of the **small intestine**, or **ileum**, joins the large intestine.
The appendix is attached to the cecum.

cell ▶ page 29

cerebellum *noun*
The cerebellum is one of the three main parts of the **brain**. It is found just behind and above the **brain stem**. The cerebellum co-ordinates body movements, balance, and posture.
She found it hard to balance because of damage to her cerebellum.

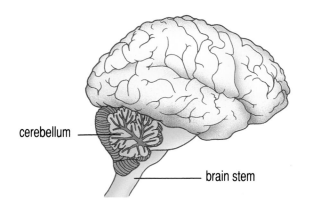
cerebellum — brain stem

cerebral cortex *noun*
The cerebral cortex is part of the **brain**. It forms the outer layer of each part of the **cerebrum** and has a gray color. The cerebral cortex directs voluntary movement. It also receives and acts on messages from the **sense** organs. Functions such as **intelligence** and **memory** also involve the cerebral cortex.
The cerebral cortex is also known as gray matter.

cell *noun*
A cell is the basic unit of all living matter.
A cell is made up of a central **nucleus** which is surrounded by **cytoplasm**. The cell is covered by cell membrane. A baby starts life as a single fertilized cell, which divides into more cells as the **embryo** develops. As the embryo grows, different kinds of cells appear, forming **skin**, **bones**, **nerves** and other parts of the body. Cells continue to divide in their different forms throughout a person's life.
An adult human body contains about 10 trillion cells.
cellular *adjective*

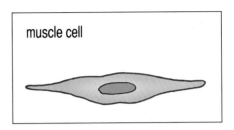

muscle cell

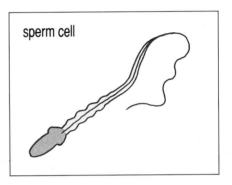

sperm cell

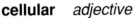

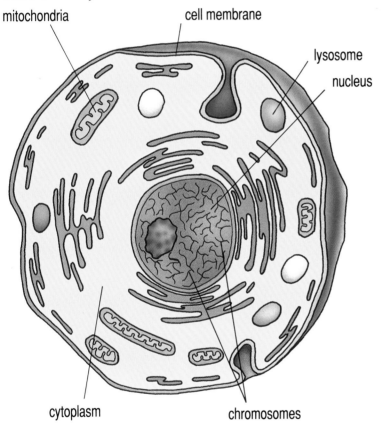

A human cell

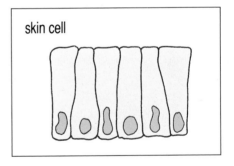

skin cell

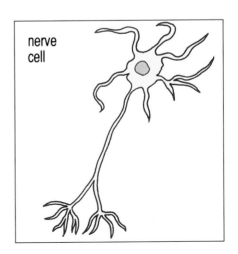

nerve cell

Cells in the human body are specialized according to the job they do. There are at least 100 different kinds of cells in the human body. They are all different shapes and sizes.

cerebral palsy   *noun*
Cerebral palsy is a disorder of the brain that affects posture and movement. People with cerebral palsy may not be able to speak very well, and often walk with jerky movements. Many people with cerebral palsy have normal intelligence but have difficulty with movement and communication. This kind of brain damage usually occurs before birth. It can also happen during birth or soon after a baby is born.
Cerebral palsy may be caused by a disease, an accident, or illness during pregnancy.

cerebrum   *noun*
The cerebrum is the largest part of the **brain**. It is sometimes called the forebrain, as it sits in the front of the head, underneath the skull. The cerebrum is made up of two half circles, or hemispheres, of soft tissue. This part of the brain controls thought and actions. It also sends messages to the **sense** organs.
Speech is controlled by three areas in the left hemisphere of the cerebrum.

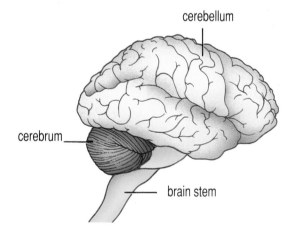

cerebellum

cerebrum

brain stem

cervical vertebrae   *noun*
The cervical vertebrae are the top seven bones of the **spine**. These small, ring-shaped bones sit on top of one another to form the **neck**. The two top cervical vertebrae are called the **atlas** and the **axis**. They are able to swivel around, allowing the head to turn.
The cervical vertebrae are held in place by ligaments.

cervix   *noun*
A cervix is another word for a **neck**. It can also refer to the neck of an **organ**. The cervix of the **uterus** is a narrow passageway between the uterus and the **vagina**.
When a baby is ready to be born, the cervix widens to allow it to pass through.
cervical   adjective

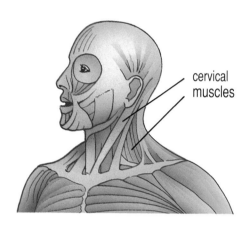

cervical muscles

Cesarean section   *noun*
A Cesarean section is an **operation** to deliver a baby. It is done under general or local **anesthetic**, so that the mother feels no pain. A doctor cuts through the wall of the mother's abdomen into the **uterus** to take out the baby. If her pelvis is too narrow for the baby to pass through, the mother must have a Cesarean section. If the baby is in the wrong position, it may be easier and safer to deliver the baby by Cesarean section.
A Cesarean section may be performed if the mother is not well.

characteristic   *noun*
1. A characteristic is an essential feature of something.
A sore throat and a stuffy nose are characteristics of a cold.
2. A characteristic is a typical feature of something else. A nose is a facial characteristic. A sense of humor is a characteristic of personality.
When she saw the characteristic spots, the doctor knew the child had chickenpox.
characteristic   adjective

check-up   *noun*
A check-up is a visit to the doctor to find out if the patient has any health problems. The doctor may ask a lot of questions and listen to a patient's chest and heart. Taking **blood pressure** and performing a **blood test** and a **urine** test are all part of a check-up.
He had to have a thorough check-up before starting to train as a pilot.

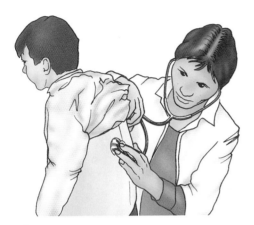

cheek   *noun*
Cheeks are the fleshy parts covering the face from below the eyes down to the jaw. They form the outside walls of the mouth, and they protect the cheekbones.
The skin on the baby's cheeks was smooth and soft.

chemotherapy   *noun*
Chemotherapy is a way of treating a disease, especially **cancer**, with drugs. Chemicals that work against the infection or malignant cells are swallowed, or injected into the body.
The chemotherapy involved a mixture of several different drugs.

chest   *noun*
The chest is the part of the body between the neck and the abdomen. It is also called the **thorax**. The frame of the chest is formed by 12 pairs of **ribs** which join onto the **spine**. The **heart** and **lungs** are located in the chest.
The muscles of the diaphragm form the base of the chest.

chew   *verb*
Chewing is the action of grinding food between teeth. Chewing breaks down the food into small particles, and helps to mix it with **saliva** before it is swallowed.
He had to chew the tough piece of meat for a long time.

chickenpox   *noun*
Chickenpox is a common childhood **disease** caused by a **virus**. It is not usually a serious illness. The virus is very easy to catch, and spreads quickly from one child to another. The first symptoms are a slight temperature, runny nose, and sore throat. Then an itchy, red rash appears over the body. The spots soon turn into blisters, which dry up into scabs after a few days. The scabs may take another week to fall off, and they may leave scars.
The itching of chickenpox spots can be soothed by calamine lotion.

chilblain   *noun*
A chilblain is a small, inflamed patch of skin that happens in cold, wet weather. Parts of the body which are most likely to suffer from chilblains are toes, fingers, ears and face. The skin becomes reddish-blue and swollen. It is painful, itchy and has a burning feeling. Keeping warm and dry is the best treatment for chilblains.
He wore two pairs of socks to avoid getting chilblains on his toes.

child   *noun*
A child is a young human who is growing to be an **adult**. Childhood begins when a baby is learning to walk and talk, and lasts until he or she starts to become sexually mature in **adolescence**. Children grow rapidly during their childhood, both physically and mentally. It is a time for playing and learning all about the world around them.
The five-year-old child was learning to read at school.

childbirth ► page 32

childbirth   *noun*

Childbirth is the act of giving birth. Birth in humans occurs about nine months after the **embryo** first begins to grow inside the mother. Birth is the moment when a baby enters the world and becomes separate from its mother.

Most babies are born head-first during childbirth.

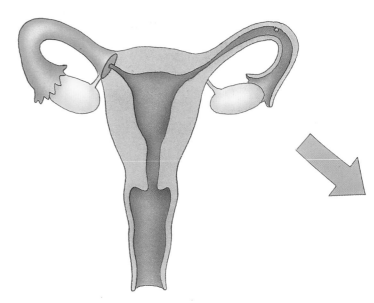

An ovum is fertilized by a sperm. The ovum starts to develop almost immediately.

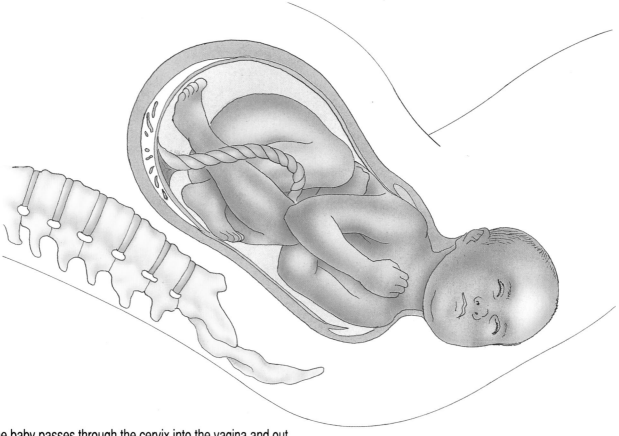

The baby passes through the cervix into the vagina and out of the mother's body.

The ovum travels down the Fallopian tube and embeds itself in the uterus.

Under eight weeks, the developing baby is called an embryo. After that time, it is called a fetus. When it is 12 weeks old, its arms, legs, hands, and feet have formed, and the skeleton is developing.

The fetus lies in a bag filled with amniotic fluid. The placenta connects the bag with the uterus. The fetus obtains food and oxygen through the umbilical cord which is attached to the placenta.

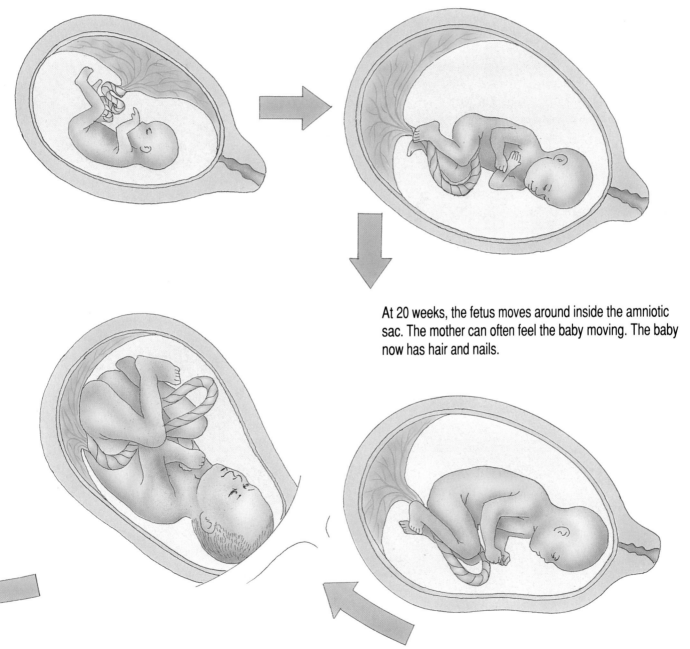

At 20 weeks, the fetus moves around inside the amniotic sac. The mother can often feel the baby moving. The baby now has hair and nails.

At 38 weeks, the baby lies upside down, ready to be born. It now fills the uterus.

chill *noun*
A chill is the feeling of being cold. It is also an attack of **shivering**. Having a chill with shivers can be a symptom of an illness.
He caught a chill after sitting in the cold hall all afternoon.

chin *noun*
The chin is part of the lower **jawbone**, below the mouth.
Some men have hair growing on their chin and cheeks.

chiropractic *noun*
Chiropractic is a kind of **alternative medicine** that involves moving the bones in the **spine**. Someone who practices chiropractic is called a chiropractor. Chiropractors use their hands to gently adjust the position of the **vertebrae**.
Chiropractic can be used to relieve pain in joints and muscles.

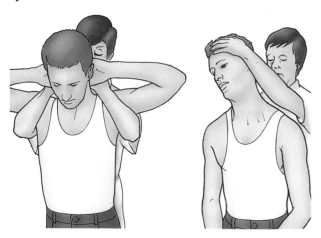

cholera *noun*
Cholera is an **infectious disease**, found mainly in South America, Asia, and Africa. It is caused by drinking water or eating food that is infected with cholera **bacteria**, which attack the **small intestine** and cause severe **vomiting** and **diarrhea**. Cholera is a life-threatening disease, but people can recover from cholera in two weeks if it is treated in time. A disease that spreads quickly like cholera is called an **epidemic**.
In areas where cholera is widespread, people should boil their drinking water.

cholesterol *noun*
Cholesterol is a fatty substance used by the body to help digest food. The body makes its own cholesterol in the **liver**. It is also found in foods such as butter, eggs, and meat. Too much cholesterol in the **blood** can cause blockage and hardening of the **arteries**, which can lead to problems with the **heart**.
Lowering cholesterol levels in the blood can help to reduce the risk of heart attacks.

chromosome *noun*
A chromosome is a tiny, thread-like part in the **nucleus** of a **cell** that carries all kinds of information about a person. Hundreds of **genes** in each chromosome store details such as the color of eyes and hair. The chromosomes in the cells of a baby are a mixture of its parents' genes. This is why children often look like both their mother and father.
There are 23 pairs of chromosomes in each human cell.

chronic *adjective*
Chronic describes an illness or pain that lasts a long time and changes very little. The opposite of chronic is **acute**.
Rheumatoid arthritis is a chronic disease.

circulation *noun*
The circulation is the flow of **blood** around the body. Blood passes from the heart through **arteries**. It flows back to the heart through **veins**.
She had such poor circulation that her toes turned blue in the cold.

circulatory system   *noun*
The circulatory system is the network of **veins** and **arteries** in the body. The heart, blood, and blood vessels are parts of this network. Veins and arteries are strong, flexible tubes that carry blood to all parts of the body. Blood contains **nutrients** from food and **oxygen** which the body needs. It also takes away **waste products**, such as carbon dioxide and urea, to be flushed out of the system.
Hormones are taken around the body by the blood in the circulatory system.

circumcision   *noun*
Circumcision is a small operation that is performed on the **penis**. Part or all of the **foreskin** is removed. Baby boys are often circumcised for reasons of hygiene, or because of religious tradition. Circumcision in an older child or in an adult is less common, and is usually carried out because the foreskin is too tight.
A penis works the same way, whether it has been circumcised or not.

clavicle ► **collarbone**

clinic   *noun*
A clinic is a place that provides health advice and treatment. People visit clinics if they are ill and want to see a doctor. Patients can be treated in a clinic if they do not need to stay in a hospital. Some clinics are attached to hospitals, and some clinics deal with certain types of cases, such as women's health problems.
Doctors in local clinics help people with every sort of disorder.

clitoris   *noun*
The clitoris is part of the genitals of a female. It is a small piece of soft tissue just below the pubic bone. The folds of the vaginal lips, called the **labia**, protect this sensitive part of the body.
The clitoris becomes larger as a girl becomes sexually mature.

clot   *noun*
A clot is a substance like jelly that forms when a liquid thickens. **Blood** contains special substances to make a clot, in order to stop bleeding. Some people do not have the necessary substances in their blood to make clots; they are called hemophiliacs.
A blood clot formed at the wound, and the bleeding stopped.

clubfoot   *noun*
Clubfoot is a **congenital** deformity of the **foot** in which the sole of the foot turns inwards and the heel points upward. A clubfoot must be set in the right position with a plaster cast or a metal brace, until it grows properly.
A bad case of clubfoot can be corrected by an operation.

coccyx   *noun*
The coccyx is the last bone at the bottom of the spine. Also called the tailbone, it is made up of four small bones joined, or fused, together.
In children, the four vertebrae of the coccyx are separate.

cochlea   *noun*
The cochlea is the **inner ear**. It is a **cavity**, or space, that is shaped like a spiral and filled with fluid. **Sensory nerves** in the cochlea pick up sounds and send messages to the **brain**. The cochlea also helps a person to balance.
Inside the cochlea are three tubes filled with liquid.

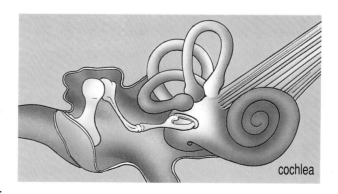
cochlea

cold *noun*
A cold is an infection caused by a **virus**. It is very easy to catch a cold from another person. A runny nose, headache, sore throat, and cough are all **symptoms** of a cold. Ordinary colds are not serious and only last a few days. There is no cure for a cold, but the symptoms can be treated with medicines.
Children catch colds more often than adults.

collagen *noun*
Collagen is the gluey kind of **protein** that makes up **connective tissue**, such as **tendons**. Collagen is also found in skin, bone, cartilage, and ligaments.
Damage to collagen development can result in fragile, rubbery skin and loose joints.

collarbone *noun*
The collarbone, or clavicle, connects the **scapula** and **sternum**. It is shaped like an upside-down coat hanger and runs from shoulder to shoulder in the front of the body. You can feel your collarbone on either side of the bottom of your neck.
When he broke his collarbone, he had to wear a sling.

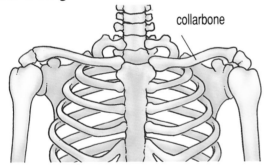

collarbone

colon *noun*
The colon is the widest part of the **intestine**, stretching from the **cecum** to the **rectum**. The walls of the colon absorb water and salts from digested food. These are taken away by the blood and used by the body. The waste matter, or **feces**, that are left behind are stored in the rectum until they are ready to be passed through the **anus**.
The strong muscles in the colon push feces along the intestine.

colostrum ► **breast-feeding**

color blindness *noun*
Color blindness is a **congenital** disorder of the **eyes**. If it is complete, people cannot recognize any colors at all. People with partial color blindness have difficulty telling some colors from others.
Color blindness is more common in men than in women.

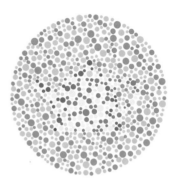

coma *noun*
A coma is a state of deep **unconsciousness** caused by illness or injury. Comas can last days, weeks, or months. Someone in a coma must be looked after in a hospital.
Patients with diabetes can fall into a coma if their illness is not treated.

conception *noun*
Conception is a stage in sexual reproduction. It is the moment a male **sperm** fertilizes a female **egg** in a woman's **Fallopian tube**. The fertilized egg then moves into the **uterus** where it grows into an **embryo**.
Within one day after conception, the egg begins to divide and grow.

concussion *noun*
Concussion is an injury to the **brain** caused by a blow or an accident. Someone with a concussion has usually been made **unconscious**. On waking up, he or she may feel nauseous and have a headache. Concussions require treatment by a doctor.
He suffered a mild concussion when he fell off the ladder.

cone ► eye

congenital   *adjective*
Congenital describes a disorder that a person is born with. It can be a disease or a deformity. Some congenital disorders are not serious, such as **color blindness**. Others are more serious, such as **heart disease** or **deafness**. Congenital disorders occur when a **fetus** does not develop properly.
Down's syndrome is a congenital disorder.

conjunctiva   *noun*
The conjunctiva is a thin **mucous membrane** that covers the front of the **eye** and lines the inside of the **eyelid**.
The conjunctiva produces a fluid that moistens and protects the eyeball.

conjunctivitis   *noun*
Conjunctivitis is an inflammation of the **conjunctiva** of the eye. Someone with a cold or influenza may develop conjunctivitis. The white of the eye becomes bloodshot and sore. The eyes water and are sensitive to bright light. Conjunctivitis may be caused by an **allergy**, or by **bacteria** or **viruses**.
Conjunctivitis caused by bacteria can be treated with antibiotic eye drops.

connective tissue   *noun*
Connective tissue joins and holds parts of the body together. **Tendons** and **ligaments** are different kinds of connective tissue. They connect and support **bones** and **muscles**.
Connective tissue binds together bunches of muscle fiber.

constipation   *noun*
Constipation is a bowel condition. A person has constipation when he or she finds it difficult to pass out **feces** through the **anus**. How often the body needs to pass feces varies from person to person. Some people have bowel movements every day, others only three times a week.
Eating fiber helps to prevent constipation.

contact lens   *noun*
A contact lens is a round piece of plastic that fits directly over the **cornea** of the **eye**, to correct a sight defect. Some people wear contact lenses instead of eyeglasses. Unlike eyeglasses, contact lenses move as the eye moves, floating on a film of tears. There are two kinds of contact lens — hard and soft. Both kinds are usually taken out at bedtime.
He kept his soft contact lenses in all day.

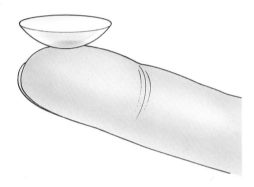

contagious   *adjective*
Contagious describes a **disease** that is caught from another person, either by touching that person, or by contact with cups, plates, or other objects used by an infected person. Animals, such as rats, and insects, such as flies, can also spread contagious diseases.
Chickenpox, measles, and influenza are all contagious diseases.
contagion   *noun*

contraception   *noun*
Contraception is a way of stopping a **sperm** from fertilizing an **ovum** to make a baby. It is used by men and women who want to choose whether they have children, or how many. There are many different ways of preventing conception. Fitting a special cap over the **cervix** stops sperm from entering the **uterus**. A rubber sheath, or condom, can also be used to catch the sperm.
Birth control pills are another method of contraception.
contraceptive   *noun and adjective*

convulsion *noun*
A convulsion is a fit of muscle **spasms**. Someone having a convulsion is usually **unconscious**, and his or her body jerks violently as the muscles contract and relax. A high **fever** can cause convulsions, especially in children under two years old. **Epilepsy** also causes convulsions. Convulsions are not harmful in themselves, and a person recovers quickly.
They moved the furniture to prevent her from hurting herself during the convulsion.

coordination *noun*
Coordination means being able to time movements in the right order. Walking needs coordination, because every part of each leg has to move to the right place at the right time. The **cerebellum** controls the body's coordination.
The ballet dancer needed superb coordination to perform dramatic leaps.

corn *noun*
A corn is a small area of thick skin on the foot. Hard corns are painful when the core inside presses on a nerve. Corns between the toes are soft and sometimes become inflamed. Most corns are caused by wearing shoes that do not fit properly. Hard corns can be removed by a chiropodist, a person who treats foot problems.
Corn plasters are used to relieve pain from corns.

cornea *noun*
The cornea is part of the **eyeball**. It is the clear layer of **membrane** that covers the front of the eye, underneath the **conjunctiva**. Light rays focus through the cornea to the **lens** of the eye.
There are no blood vessels in the cornea.

coronary *adjective*
Coronary is a word that describes anything to do with the heart.
Coronary arteries supply blood to the heart.

coronary heart disease ► heart disease

coronary thrombosis *noun*
A coronary thrombosis occurs when the coronary **arteries** become blocked, usually by a blood **clot**, and the blood supply to the heart is partly or completely cut off. People can recover from a mild coronary thrombosis, but more serious ones are fatal. It is also called a heart attack.
Regular exercise and a healthy diet can reduce the risk of coronary thrombosis.

corpuscle *noun*
A corpuscle is a **cell** or other small, rounded body.
Red and white blood cells are corpuscles.

cortex *noun*
A cortex is the outer layer of an **organ**. The outer layer of the brain is called the **cerebral cortex**.
The adrenal cortex secretes three types of hormones.

cortisone *noun*
Cortisone is a **hormone** that is made in the outer layer, or **cortex**, of the **adrenal gland**. The liver turns cortisone into cortisol, which helps to control **glucose**, fats, and water in the body. Doctors use an **artificial** cortisone to treat a number of diseases.
She had a series of cortisone injections to relieve her arthritis.

cough *noun*
A cough is a sudden push of air out of the **lungs**. It is the body's way of clearing the lungs or **throat**. A cough may be a **symptom** of a **disease** or **illness**, such as a chest **infection** or **asthma**.
The smoky atmosphere made him cough.

cramp *noun*
A cramp is a sudden tightening, or **spasm**, in a **muscle**, which causes pain. Too much exercise can cause cramps. Sweating and losing a lot of body fluids is another reason for cramps to occur. Gently stretching and warming the muscle helps to ease a cramp.
The athlete had a cramp in her leg after the race.

cranium ► **skull**

croup *noun*
Croup is a breathing disorder. It is most common in children aged between one and four years. Virus infections are the main cause of croup. The **lungs**, **throat**, and **voice box** become inflamed and swollen. Children with croup have a hoarse cough that sounds like a bark. They have a **fever**, and cannot breathe easily. If a croup attack is mild, a child can be treated at home. A steamy atmosphere will ease the breathing.
His attack of croup lasted three days.

crown *noun*
A crown is the part of a tooth you can see. A dentist can fit an **artificial** crown on to a damaged tooth. These artificial crowns are usually made of gold covered by white porcelain.
The artificial crown that the dentist made blended in perfectly with the boy's other teeth.

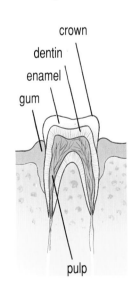

crown
dentin
enamel
gum
pulp

cut *noun*
A cut is an opening in the skin made by a sharp object. When the skin is cut, the body bleeds. Pressing firmly on a cut stops the bleeding. If **germs** enter a cut, it may become **infected**. When a cut is long and deep, it may need to be stitched up by a doctor. This helps it to heal. A surgeon makes a cut in the skin during an **operation**, using a special knife called a scalpel.
Most cuts heal very quickly by themselves.

cuticle *noun*
The cuticle is an outer layer of **skin**. It is also the tough skin found at the base of **fingernails** or **toenails**.
She had a manicure to trim the cuticles of her fingernails.

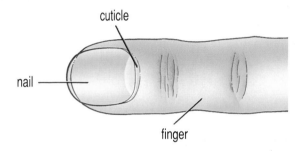

cuticle
nail
finger

cyst *noun*
A cyst is a swelling or lump filled with fluid. Cysts commonly form in the **skin**, **breasts**, and **ovaries**. They can develop if a gland becomes blocked. Most cysts are **benign** and do not lead to serious illness. In some cases, a doctor drains the fluid from a cyst with a needle, and the swelling disappears.
If a cyst is large or painful, it can be removed by an operation.

deafness   noun

Deafness means not being able to hear well or not being able to hear at all. It can affect one or both ears. People can be born deaf, or deafness can develop in later life. Elderly people often develop some deafness. Partial deafness can be helped by a hearing aid.
The deaf boy learned to communicate by using sign language.

death   noun

Death is the end of life. When people live for a long time, parts of their body stop working and they eventually die. This is part of the **aging** process. Death can also be caused by an illness or an accident.
Accidents are a leading cause of death among young people.

dehydration   noun

Dehydration is the result of losing too much water from the body. Severe **diarrhea**, **vomiting**, and **sweating** cause dehydration. Very hot weather or having a high fever may make someone sweat too much.
People suffering from dehydration should drink plenty of liquids.

dementia   noun

Dementia is a brain illness. A person with dementia cannot remember things or think clearly. Eventually, he or she may have a change of personality. Elderly people sometimes develop dementia, as a result of **aging**, or it can be caused by a **tumor** in the brain.
Her dementia made her confuse nighttime with daytime.

dental   adjective

Dental is a word that describes anything to do with **teeth**. Dentists look after people's teeth and gums.
The dental hygienist assisted the dentist with the fillings.

dentin   noun

Dentin is the main part of a **tooth**. It is the hard substance that surrounds the soft pulp at the tooth's center. Dentin is covered by a layer of tough **enamel**. Enamel is the white, outer part of the tooth that can be seen.
Dentin is harder than bone.

dentist   noun

A dentist is someone who looks after people's **teeth**, **mouth**, and **gums**. Dentists drill away decay in teeth and fill in the cavities. They take out badly decayed teeth and put in **artificial**, or false, teeth. Dentists tell people how to avoid tooth decay by eating a good diet and cleaning their teeth properly.
Dentists advise people to have a dental check-up at least once a year.

dentition   noun

Dentition is the development of **teeth**. Babies' teeth appear during their first year. These first teeth are called baby teeth. There are 20 baby teeth. These start to become loose and fall out one by one from about the age of six years. They are gradually replaced with a set of 32 adult teeth, and dentition is complete.
Dentition made the baby dribble.

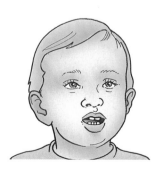

depression *noun*
Depression is a mental disorder. People suffering from depression may feel sad or helpless. They often lose interest in what is going on around them. Depression can be treated by psychotherapy or **drugs**.
While she was suffering from depression, she kept bursting into tears.

dermatitis *noun*
Dermatitis is an **inflammation** of the **skin**. The symptoms are dry, itchy patches of red skin, which can become very sore if the skin breaks and becomes infected. Dermatitis may develop when the skin has been in contact with a chemical substance, such as detergent or acid. Some metals and a few plants also cause dermatitis.
Dermatitis can be treated with special creams.

dermis *noun*
The dermis is the middle layer of the **skin**. It lies below the top layer of skin, or **epidermis**. The dermis contains connective tissue, blood vessels, nerve endings, and hair follicles.
The dermis is thicker than the epidermis.

develop *verb*
Develop is another word for grow. Children develop into adults. To develop also means to change and become something else. For example, a cold may develop into pneumonia.
She developed a rash after lying in the sun.

diabetes *noun*
Diabetes is the name for two separate disorders. Diabetes insipidus is caused by the lack of a **hormone** called ADH. Diabetes mellitus is caused by the lack of an essential hormone called **insulin**. People who suffer from diabetes are called diabetics. The **symptoms** of diabetes are passing an unusual amount of urine and feeling thirsty all the time. Without treatment, a diabetic will become very ill and fall into a **coma**.
She developed diabetes when she was eight years old.

diagnosis *noun*
A diagnosis is the decision a doctor makes about what kind of disorder his or her patient is suffering from. To make a diagnosis, the doctor looks for **symptoms**. Patients are examined and asked questions about how they feel. They may also have medical tests, such as an **X-ray** or a **blood test**.
Doctors make a diagnosis so that they can give a patient the right treatment.
diagnose *verb*

dialysis *noun*
Dialysis is a method of cleaning the blood with a machine. This job is usually done by the **kidneys**, and a dialysis machine works like a kidney. Blood is let out of an **artery** and into the machine. It passes through a filter which takes out unwanted substances, then the clean blood is fed back into a **vein**. Dialysis usually needs to be carried out three times a week.
Cleaning all of a patient's blood by dialysis takes between four and six hours.

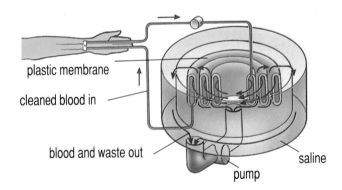

plastic membrane
cleaned blood in
blood and waste out
saline
pump

diaphragm *noun*
The diaphragm is a large sheet of **muscle** that separates the organs in the **abdomen** from the heart and lungs in the chest. The diaphragm is the important muscle used for breathing. It tightens and becomes flat to draw breath into the lungs. Air is pushed out when the diaphragm relaxes and expands upward in a curve.
The diaphragm muscle is shaped like a dome.

digestion   *noun*

Digestion is the breaking down of **food** in the body. Food starts to be digested as soon as it enters the mouth. It is broken down into smaller and smaller pieces as it travels through the digestive system. The digestive organs include the **stomach**, the **small intestine** and the **large intestine**.
Vitamins and minerals do not need digestion, as they are absorbed straight into the bloodstream.

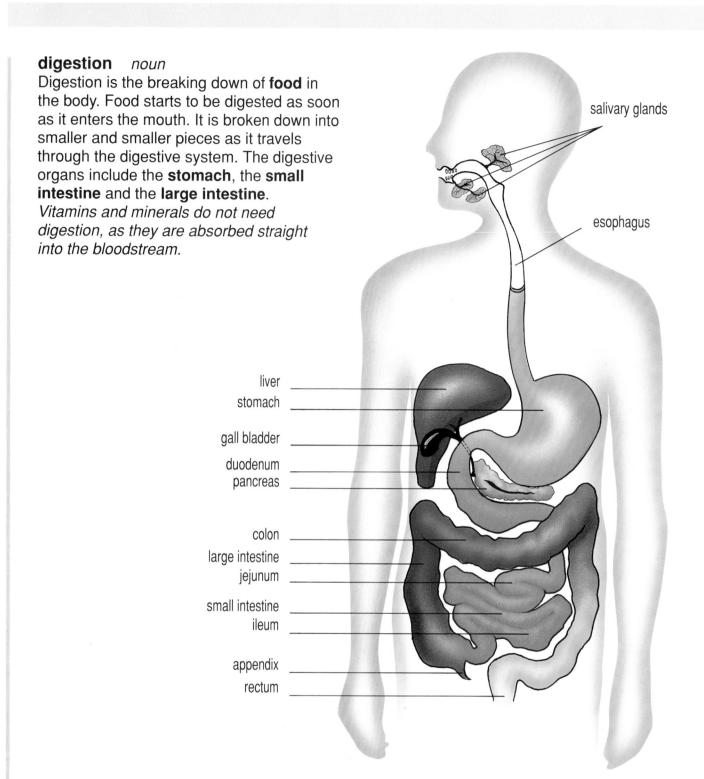

salivary glands

esophagus

liver
stomach
gall bladder
duodenum
pancreas
colon
large intestine
jejunum
small intestine
ileum
appendix
rectum

1. As food is ground by the teeth, it is mixed with saliva. Saliva is produced by three glands in the face and contains enzymes. Each mouthful of food is rolled into a ball that is easy to swallow.

2. The ball of food travels down the esophagus to the stomach. The elastic walls of the stomach expand as it fills with food. Gastric juices from glands in the stomach wall mix with the food and start to digest it. The juices contain hydrochloric acid. The stomach churns to mix the contents thoroughly. Food stays in the stomach between two and five hours.

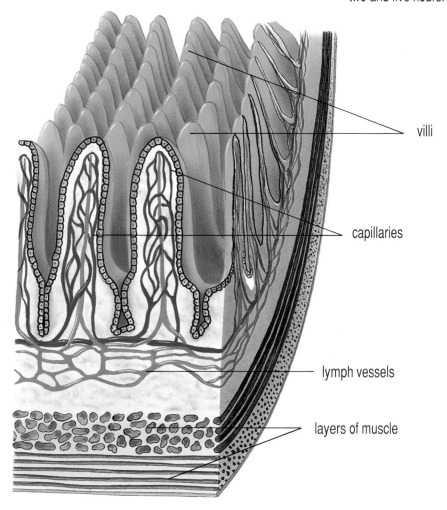

villi

capillaries

lymph vessels

layers of muscle

3. The partly digested food is now a thick liquid called chyme. Chyme enters the duodenum where it is mixed with juices from the pancreas, liver, and gall bladder.

4. In the jejunum and the ileum, nutrients from digested food are absorbed into the bloodstream.

5. Digestion is almost complete by the time food reaches the large intestine. The undigested food is pushed down the colon where water and some minerals are absorbed.

6. Bacteria feed on the waste and turn it into feces, which then pass down the rectum, and out through the anus.

The walls of the small intestine are lined with tiny fingers called villi which make the surface look like velvet. Villi contain blood capillaries and other vessels that contain lymph. The lymph vessels absorb fat and the capillaries take nutrients from the digested food into the bloodstream.

diarrhea *noun*
Diarrhea is soft, liquid **feces** that are passed frequently. It can be the result of a mild stomach upset or it may be a **symptom** of a more serious disease. Diarrhea makes the body lose water, which can cause **dehydration**. People with diarrhea should drink plenty of fluids.
He had diarrhea after eating the shellfish.

diet *noun*
1. A diet is the mixture of foods a person eats every day. To keep the body healthy, a diet must include **proteins**, **carbohydrates**, **fats**, **vitamins**, **fiber**, and **minerals**.
A varied diet gives the body all the nourishment it needs.
2. A diet is a way of controlling the intake of food. People may go on a diet because they want to lose weight. Some people who suffer from certain diseases follow a special diet.
After his heart attack, his doctor recommended a low-fat diet.

digestion ► page 42

diphtheria *noun*
Diphtheria is an **infectious disease** that mainly affects breathing. It is more common in children under the age of 10. Diphtheria is caused by **bacteria** that grow in the nose and throat. It is now rare because of **vaccination**, which is given to babies in their first year of life to protect them.
Doctors recommend three doses of diphtheria vaccine in the first year.

disability *noun*
A disability is the loss of function or use of part of the body. Some people are born with a disability, and some acquire it through accident or illness. The disability may be mental or physical. Special equipment and other aids help disabled people to live as normal a life as possible.
Her disability did not stop her from joining the team.
disabled *adjective*

disease ► page 45

disinfectant *noun*
Disinfectant is a chemical used to kill **germs**. Destroying germs stops the spread of infection. People put disinfectant in water to wash areas such as floors and toilets where germs are found.
She washed the thermometer in disinfectant after taking his temperature.

disk *noun*
A disk is a round, flat, plate-shaped object. In the body, the optic disk is found at the back of the **eye**. Another kind of disk lies between each pair of **vertebrae** in the **spine**. These act as cushions between the bones, and allow the spine to bend easily.
Spinal disks are made of cartilage with a soft, jellylike center.

dislocation *noun*
Dislocation describes what happens when bones in a **joint** are knocked or twisted out of place. This can happen through an accident or injury, and causes great pain. A doctor should be called to put the joint back in place.
Shoulders are the most common joints to suffer dislocation.

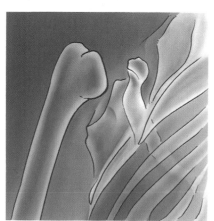

An X-ray of a dislocated shoulder

dissect *verb*
Dissect means to cut up carefully. Students dissect parts of plants and animals to learn about their **anatomy**.
She dissected the dead mouse to examine its lungs.
dissection *noun*

disease *noun*

Disease is a sickness in some part of the body or the mind. Many people have mild diseases such as colds, and recover from them. Other diseases can be incurable, or fatal. Sometimes people have a disease that they have inherited. Some diseases are **infectious**. Other diseases happen when the body or mind is damaged in some way. *The builder developed lung disease from working with asbestos.*

Muscular dystrophy is an inherited disease. It causes gradual weakening of the muscles until a person can no longer move around independently.

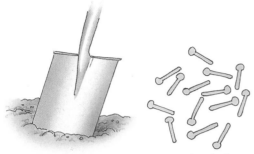

tetanus bacteria

Some diseases, such as tetanus, develop when bacteria enter the body through a cut in the skin. Tetanus bacteria may be found in the soil.

leukemia cells

Leukemia is a disease of the blood. It is a type of cancer and is not infectious.

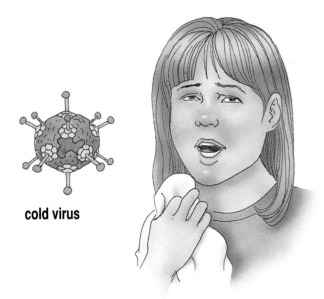

cold virus

Infectious diseases are spread by people, by animals and insects, and other objects such as food. Colds are easily spread to other people.

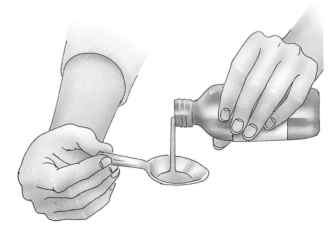

Diseases are treated in many different ways. The body's immune system fights disease, or a doctor may prescribe drugs or surgery. Many diseases can be prevented by good hygiene, a healthy lifestyle, and immunization.

dizziness *noun*
Dizziness is a feeling of being light-headed and unsteady. It may occur when a person's sense of balance is upset, or when not enough blood reaches the brain. Repeated attacks of dizziness may be a **symptom** of an illness.
Feeling hungry or tired sometimes causes dizziness.

DNA *noun*
DNA is a chemical found in the center, or **nucleus**, of every **cell**. The letters DNA stand for deoxyribonucleic acid. DNA stores **genetic** information and passes it on to new cells. This genetic information provides the master plan, or blueprint, of each person, including every detail of how a person is put together, and what he or she looks like.
Everyone except identical twins has different DNA.

doctor *noun*
A doctor is a person who looks after people when they are ill, and helps them to keep healthy. Men and women have special medical training to become doctors. Family doctors deal with all kinds of health problems. Other doctors, or specialists, treat only certain kinds of illness, or groups of people. For example, a specialist doctor who looks after children is called a pediatrician.
A long period of training is necessary to become a doctor.

dorsal *adjective*
Dorsal describes the back, or **posterior**, of any part of the body. The opposite of dorsal is **ventral**.
Dorsal roots lie at the back of the spinal cord.

dose *noun*
A dose is a measure of **medicine**. All **drugs** and medicines are carefully mixed and measured. If a person is taking medicine he or she must have the right dose.
He had to take a dose of medicine three times a day.

Down's syndrome *noun*
Down's syndrome is a **congenital** disorder. People with Down's syndrome have an extra **chromosome** in their cells, which makes them physically and mentally less able than other people. People with Down's syndrome take much longer to learn how to do things for themselves. However, with special training and support, they can hold jobs and lead enjoyable lives.
Down's syndrome is also known as Mongolism.

dream ► sleep

drug *noun*
A drug is a chemical substance used to prevent or treat illnesses. Organic drugs are found in plants or other living material. Synthetic drugs are made from **artificial** substances. Drugs are used to make **medicines**. Because drugs are harmful if they are not used properly, they should be taken only with careful supervision.
The drugs were locked up in the pharmacy until they were needed.

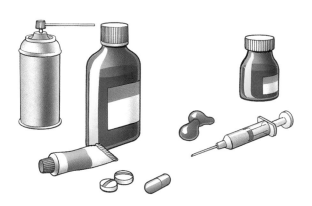

duct *noun*
A duct is a narrow tube in the body that carries fluids from one part of the body to another.
Tears flow into the eyes through the tear ducts.

duodenum *noun*
The duodenum is part of the **small intestine**. The small intestine is about 20 feet long, and the duodenum is the first part. Partly digested food passes from the **stomach** to the duodenum, where digestive juices from the **pancreas** and **gall bladder** help to break down the food.
The duodenum absorbs nutrients and water.

dysentery *noun*
Dysentery is an **inflammation** of the **large intestine**. The inflammation causes severe **diarrhea** which may contain blood and mucus. There may also be pains in the abdomen, vomiting, and fever. Dysentery is caused by **bacteria** or a **parasite**. These can be picked up by drinking contaminated water or eating infected food.
Improvements in hygiene have made dysentery much less common than it used to be.

dyslexia *noun*
Dyslexia is a specific learning disorder that affects the way a child learns how to read and write, but not his or her **intelligence**. Children with dyslexia confuse letters and find spelling difficult. Special teaching helps the condition.
Many people with dyslexia cannot tell left from right.

ear ▶ page 48

earache *noun*
Earache is a pain inside the **ear**. It can be caused by an **infection** in the middle ear or **inflammation** in the outer ear. Sudden changes in air pressure, such as in an airplane, can cause earache. Earache may also be caused by the ear being blocked with wax, or other objects.
He got an earache when he went diving.

eardrum *noun*
The eardrum is part of the **ear**. It is a thin layer of **tissue**, called the tympanic membrane, that separates the middle ear from the outer ear.
Very loud noises can damage the eardrum and cause deafness.

eat *verb*
To eat is to take food into the body through the mouth. People need to eat a balanced **diet** to stay healthy. Eating disorders include conditions called **anorexia nervosa** and **bulimia**.
A vegetarian does not eat meat.

eczema *noun*
Eczema is **inflammation** of the **skin**. It can appear anywhere on the body in children and adults. The skin develops red patches and feels itchy and sore. Most eczema is inherited, but it may also develop when the skin is in contact with chemicals, or from an allergy.
Whenever he was under stress, his eczema became worse.

ear *noun*

The ear is the organ of **hearing** and **balance**. People have two ears, one on each side of the head. The **outer ear** picks up sounds and passes them to the **middle ear** through the **eardrum.** Three tiny bones in the middle ear vibrate with the sound. These vibrations are passed to the **cochlea** in the **inner ear**, where they are changed into electric signals. The signals travel along **nerves** to the **brain**.

Hearing with two ears helps people to tell what direction a sound is coming from.

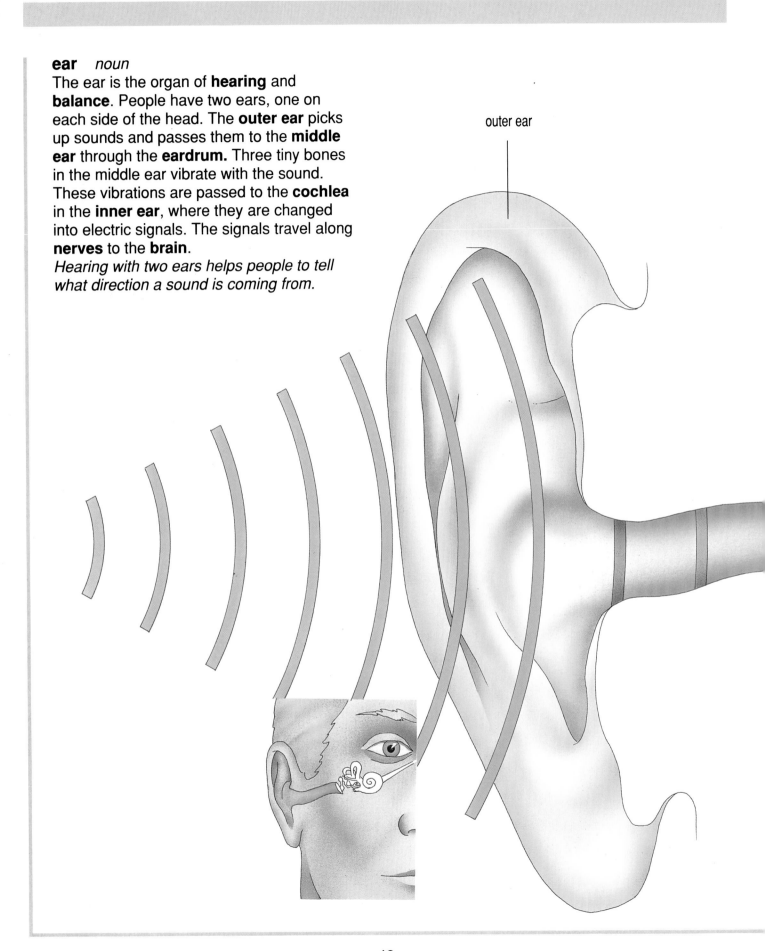

outer ear

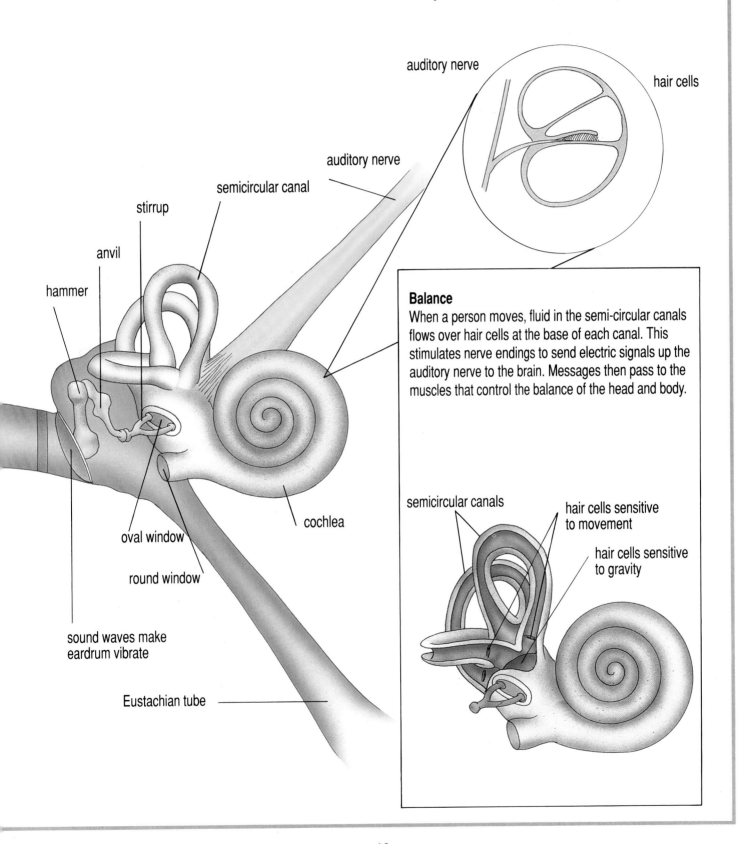

Sound vibrations move the fluid in the cochlea. This stimulates hair cells in the central section of the cochlea. Messages travel to the brain up the auditory nerve.

auditory nerve

hair cells

auditory nerve

semicircular canal

stirrup

anvil

hammer

Balance
When a person moves, fluid in the semi-circular canals flows over hair cells at the base of each canal. This stimulates nerve endings to send electric signals up the auditory nerve to the brain. Messages then pass to the muscles that control the balance of the head and body.

semicircular canals

hair cells sensitive to movement

hair cells sensitive to gravity

cochlea

oval window

round window

sound waves make eardrum vibrate

Eustachian tube

egg ▶ ovum

elbow   *noun*
The elbow is the **joint** that joins the upper and lower bones of the **arm**. This joint works like a hinge and allows the arm to bend in half. Two **muscles** in the upper arm, called the **biceps** and **triceps**, cause the arm to bend at the elbow joint.
The elbow bends in only one direction.

electrocardiograph   *noun*
An electrocardiograph is a machine that records electrical activity from the **heart**. Small metal plates called electrodes are placed on the body. The electrodes pick up electric signals, and the pattern of the signals is then recorded on a moving strip of paper. A doctor can see if a person's heart is working properly by looking at the pattern.
The electrocardiograph showed that her heart was beating normally.

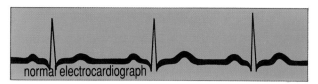
normal electrocardiograph

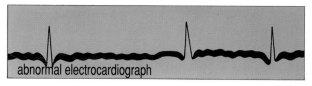
abnormal electrocardiograph

electroencephalograph   *noun*
An electroencephalograph is a machine that records electrical activity from the **brain**. This machine works in the same way as an electrocardiograph.
The electroencephalograph showed abnormal activity in the cerebellum.

elephantiasis   *noun*
Elephantiasis is a **skin** disease. It is caused when a person is bitten by a mosquito that is infected by a tiny **worm**. Rough skin develops, with **swelling** in the body, usually the legs.
Elephantiasis is most common in tropical countries.

embolism   *noun*
An embolism is a blockage of a blood vessel, such as an **artery**. The object blocking it is called an embolus. An embolus can be a bubble of air or piece of body tissue, but it is most often a blood **clot**. The clot is carried around the bloodstream until it sticks somewhere. If a blood clot becomes lodged in the blood vessels in the head, it can result in a **stroke**.
An embolism can be treated with drugs or surgery.

embryo   *noun*
An embryo is the medical name for a fertilized **ovum** that has settled into the **uterus** to grow. From the second month of **pregnancy** until the baby is born the embryo is called a **fetus**.
An embryo has tiny stumps that will grow into arms and legs.

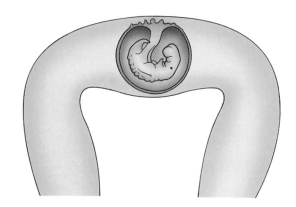

embryology   *noun*
Embryology is the study of **embryos**.
Embryology explains how an embryo grows from egg to fetus.

emphysema   *noun*
Emphysema is a disease of the **lungs** caused when the **alveoli** of the lungs do not empty out all the air in them. The lungs become over-stretched with trapped air. A person with emphysema finds it difficult to breathe and feels tightness in the chest.
Smoking cigarettes causes emphysema.

enamel *noun*
Enamel is the outer layer of a **tooth**. It is a hard, white substance that covers the part of the tooth that can be seen, or the **crown**. **Fluoride** can help to strengthen tooth enamel.
Under the tooth's enamel is found the dentin.

encephalitis *noun*
Encephalitis is an inflammation of the **brain**. It is usually caused by a **virus**. The first symptoms are a very severe headache and a fever. A person with encephalitis may feel drowsy and confused. If the illness is severe he or she may fall into a coma and have convulsions. Encephalitis can sometimes be fatal.
One kind of encephalitis is known as sleeping sickness.

endemic *adjective*
Endemic describes a **disease** that is found only in a particular place or part of the world. It also describes types of illnesses suffered only by a certain group or race of people.
Malaria is a disease that is endemic in tropical countries.

endo- *prefix*
Endo- before a word means inside or mixed in with. An endoscope is an instrument for looking inside the body. The opposite of endo- is ecto-, which means outside.
The endocardium is a membrane that lines the inside of the heart.

endocrine gland *noun*
An endocrine gland is an organ which makes **hormones** which help to control other organs in the body. These kinds of gland do not have tubes, or **ducts**, but release hormones directly into the bloodstream. Some endocrine glands also store hormones.
The thyroid is an example of an endocrine gland.

endocrine system *noun*
The endocrine system is a set of glands in the body. There are seven kinds of endocrine glands, found in the head, neck, abdomen, and genitals. The endocrine glands release **hormones** that direct many important body functions such as reproduction. The **pituitary gland** at the base of the brain controls the release of hormones into the bloodstream.
Growth and digestion are regulated by the endocrine system.

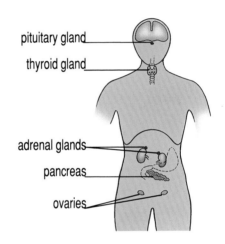

pituitary gland
thyroid gland
adrenal glands
pancreas
ovaries

endorphin *noun*
Endorphin is a **hormone** made in the brain. Endorphins are released in the body to help deaden pain. They also make a person feel happy. Exercise makes the body release endorphins to relieve aching muscles.
Endorphins help the body to cope with stress.

endoscope *noun*
An endoscope is a medical instrument used to look inside the body. It is a long, flexible tube with a light on the end. The endoscope can be pushed into a natural opening of the body, such as the nose or mouth. The stomach and lungs are often looked at in this way.
The doctor used an endoscope to examine the patient's stomach.

energy *noun*
Energy is power or strength. People burn energy like fuel. **Food** has an energy value that is measured in **calories**. Different foods have different calorie, or energy, values. An adult man needs about 2,500 calories of energy a day to live. People who are especially active, such as athletes, need more calories. People become overweight if they take in more calories than they burn up; they lose weight if they don't consume enough calories.
Extra energy is stored in the body as fat.

environment *noun*
Environment means a person's surroundings. It may be a place, such as a town. Or it may refer to living conditions, such as those found at home, school, and work. Having a clean environment, including clean air, water, and food, is important for good health. The environment must also offer warmth, shelter, and space.
An unsanitary environment increases the risk of disease.

enzyme *noun*
An enzyme is a **chemical** that joins with other chemicals to help them work faster. For example, enzymes are found in the digestive juices in the **stomach** that help break down food.
The human body contains over a thousand types of enzymes.

epi- *prefix*
Epi- before a word means over, above, or upon. The epidermis covers the dermis, or middle layer of skin.
The epithelium is a thin layer of tissue that covers surfaces inside the body.

epidemic *noun*
An epidemic is an outbreak of **infectious disease**. Epidemics spread quickly among people in the same place at the same time. **Cholera** is an epidemic disease.
An epidemic of influenza closed the school.

epidermis *noun*
The epidermis is the outer layer of the **skin**. It is a waterproof layer of **tissue** that grows new cells and sheds old ones all the time. Sweat passes through tiny openings, or **pores**, in the epidermis. Hair appears through the epidermis all over the body, apart from the palms of the hand and the soles of the feet. The epidermis covers and protects the middle layer of skin, or **dermis**.
Household dust contains old skin cells shed from the epidermis.

epididymis *noun*
The epididymis is a structure on the outside of the **testis**. It is a very thin tube about 20 feet long, coiled very tightly inside the **scrotum**. The epididymis is joined to the testis by small tubes.
Sperm matures in the epididymis.

epidural *adjective*
Epidural describes anything to do with the outer **membrane** that surrounds the **brain** and the **spinal cord**.
She was given an epidural anaesthetic before the operation.

epiglottis *noun*
The epiglottis is part of the throat. It is a thin, leaf-shaped flap that lies behind the root of the **tongue**. The epiglottis covers the opening of the **larynx** and the **trachea** during swallowing. It stops food and drink from going down the wrong way into the lungs.
Choking can result when a piece of food gets past the epiglottis into the trachea.

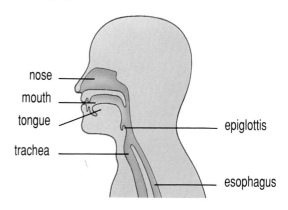

nose
mouth
tongue
trachea
epiglottis
esophagus

epilepsy *noun*
Epilepsy is a disorder of the **brain**. People who suffer from epilepsy sometimes have **convulsions**. Epilepsy may affect part or all of the brain. Partial epilepsy shows as a slight twitching in the face, arm, or leg. The person stays awake but seems far away. Generalized epilepsy leads to convulsions and loss of consciousness. Epilepsy is caused by a surge of electrical activity in the brain.
He took medication to control his epilepsy.

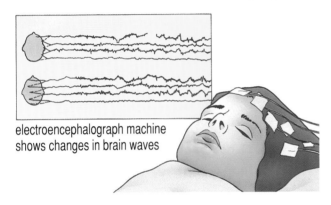

electroencephalograph machine shows changes in brain waves

equilibrium ► **balance**

erythrocyte ► **red blood cell**

esophagus *noun*
The esophagus is the tube joining the back of the **pharynx** to the **stomach.** It measures about 10 inches long. Food and drink are passed down the esophagus by muscles moving in waves. This movement is called peristalsis. Another name for the esophagus is the gullet.
Heartburn is caused by inflammation of the esophagus.

estrogen *noun*
Estrogen is a female **hormone** made by the **ovaries** and the **adrenal glands**. Estrogen helps a girl develop into a woman. It causes the breasts to develop and causes other changes at **puberty**. Estrogen also controls the monthly **menstrual cycle**.
Artificial estrogen is one of the ingredients of the contraceptive pill.

Eustachian tube *noun*
The Eustachian tube joins the back of the nose with the **middle ear**. It is about 1½ inches long. The Eustachian tube keeps the air pressure the same on each side of the **eardrum**. A blockage of the Eustachian tube can lead to a loss of hearing.
The Eustachian tube is made of bone and cartilage.

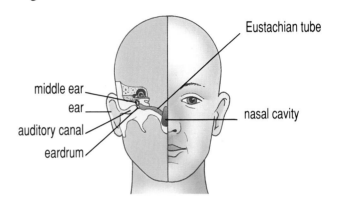

excretion *noun*
Excretion is the removal of **waste** from the body. Getting rid of **urine** and **feces** is part of the process of excretion. Sweating through the skin and breathing out carbon dioxide from the lungs is also excretion. The colon and the kidneys are also organs of excretion.
One third of a teaspoonful of salt is removed from the body by excretion every day.
excrete *verb*

exercise *noun*
Exercise is physical activity that helps to keep the body in good working order. Exercise makes people strong and flexible, and also builds stamina, which is the ability to exercise for a long time and not get tired. Doctors recommend that people exercise regularly to preserve good health. Regular exercise also makes people happier, more alert, and more relaxed.
Swimming is a good exercise for strength, stamina, and flexibility.
exercise *verb*

exhale ► **respiration**

expire ► **respiration**

53

eye *noun*
The eye is the organ of sight. People have
two eyes in front of the face. The objects
that people see give off light. Light enters the
eye through the **pupil**, and travels to the
retina. There it is converted into nerve
signals that travel to the brain.
Having two eyes helps people to judge
distances.

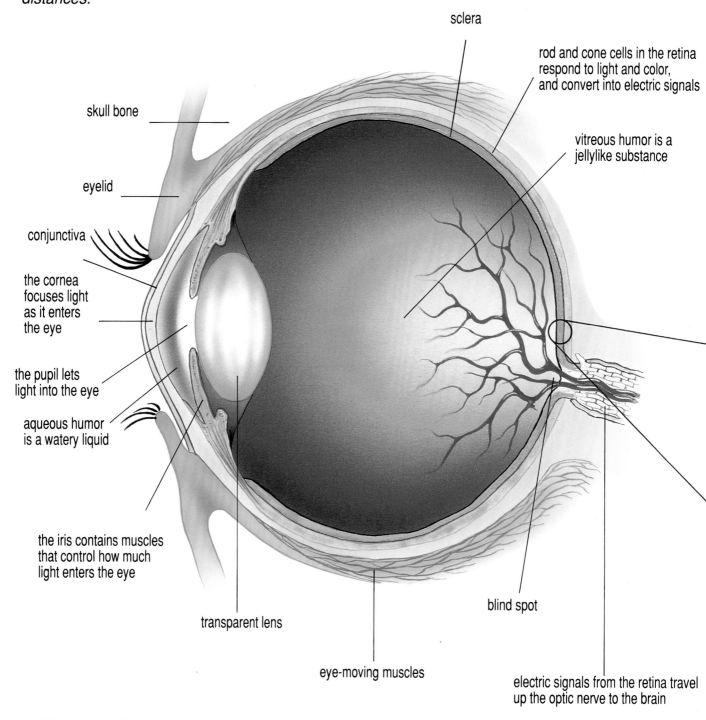

sclera

rod and cone cells in the retina
respond to light and color,
and convert into electric signals

vitreous humor is a
jellylike substance

skull bone

eyelid

conjunctiva

the cornea
focuses light
as it enters
the eye

the pupil lets
light into the eye

aqueous humor
is a watery liquid

the iris contains muscles
that control how much
light enters the eye

transparent lens

eye-moving muscles

blind spot

electric signals from the retina travel
up the optic nerve to the brain

Light rays from a distant object travel to the eye in straight lines. The cornea and the lens bend the light rays to make them come together on the retina. The lens is flat and relaxed.

Light rays from a nearby object spread out as they enter the eye. To focus the rays, the lens must bend them more sharply. The lens becomes rounder and thicker.

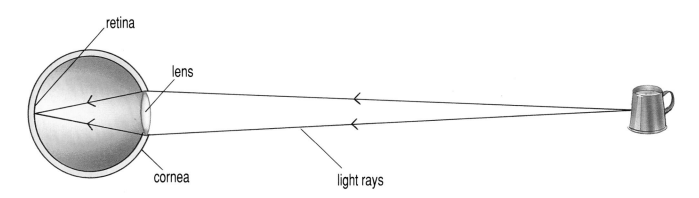

retina

lens

cornea

light rays

retina

lens

cornea

light rays

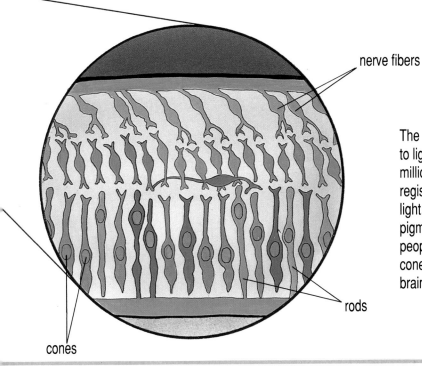

nerve fibers

cones

rods

The retina is made up of a mass of cells that are sensitive to light. There are about 120 million rod cells and about 6 million cone cells. Rods are sensitive to light, but only register shades of gray. They help people to see in dim light. The cones only work well in good light. They contain pigments that absorb green, red and blue light, and enable people to see color. Nerve fibers attached to the rods and cones carry electric signals to the optic nerve and to the brain.

external *adjective*
External describes anything outside, or the outside part of something.
The skin is an external organ of the body.

eye ► page 54

eyeball *noun*
The eyeball is the globe of the **eye**. It is almost a perfect sphere, about an inch across and filled with a jellylike substance, called **vitreous humor**. The eyeballs lie in the two spaces, or **orbits**, in the front of the skull. Three sets of **muscles** hold each eyeball in place and allow it to move around. Eyeballs are covered by a thin layer of tissue called the sclera.
Tears washed the dust off her eyeball.

eyebrow *noun*
Eyebrows are the hairy arches that curve over each **eye**. They follow the bony ridges of the top of the **orbits** in the skull where the eyeballs lie. Eyebrows help to protect the eye from dust. They also shade the eye from light.
The eyebrows are prominent features of the face.

eyelash ► **eyelid**

eyelid *noun*
Eyelids are the coverings that move up and down to protect the eyes. Both eyes in the body have top and bottom eyelids fringed with hair, or eyelashes. The eyelids are made of **skin**, **muscle**, and **connective tissue**. Eyelids blink, or close quickly, every few seconds, to keep the eye moist with **tears**. They also close the eyes during sleep.
A person blinks the eyelids once every two to ten seconds.

face *noun*
The face is the front, or **anterior**, part of the **head**. Parts, or features, of the face include the forehead, a pair of eyes, eyebrows and cheeks, a nose, mouth, and chin.
People's emotions are often visible on their face.
facial *adjective*

faint *verb*
Faint means becoming unconscious for a short time. A person may suddenly feel dizzy and weak and the next moment fall to the ground. Fainting is caused by the **brain** not getting enough blood. Falling over makes a fainting person wake up quickly as the blood. Fainting is a common **symptom** and not usually serious in itself.
She had eaten so little food, she felt she was about to faint.

Fallopian tube *noun*
The Fallopian tubes are two tubes in a woman's body. Each tube is about four inches long and attached to either side of the top of the **uterus**. **Ova**, or eggs, travel from the **ovaries** down the Fallopian tubes, helped along by tiny, hair-like **cells**.
Conception usually occurs in the Fallopian tubes.

far-sightedness *noun*
Far-sightedness is being able to see things clearly far away, but not close up. It is caused by light being focused behind the **retina** at the back of the eye instead of on it.
Wearing glasses or contact lenses helps far-sightedness.

fat *noun*
Fat is a kind of food. It gives the body **energy**, together with **protein**, and **carbohydrates**. Fat is found in butter, cream, margarine, and oil. It is also found in fatty meats, and oily fish. Fats that are not burned up and used as energy are stored in the body as fat **cells**. Some stored fats surround and protect **organs** inside the body.
Doctors recommend that people limit the amount of fat they eat.

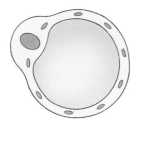

fat cells

fatigue *noun*
Fatigue is the feeling of being exhausted, or very tired. It can be tiredness of the body or of the mind. Fatigue may be caused by heavy exercise or lack of sleep. Or it may be felt by someone who is unhappy or bored. Fatigue usually disappears after rest and relaxation. A feeling of being very tired all the time, or **chronic** fatigue, is usually a **symptom** of an illness.
After the race, he was overcome by fatigue and had to rest.

fatty acid *noun*
Fatty acids are substances found in fat. They are needed to help the body produce **energy** and make use of important **vitamins**, such as A, D, E, and K. Some kinds of fatty acid are described as essential. This means that the body cannot make them but must get them from the food we eat.
She lost weight by cutting down on fatty acids in her diet.

feces *noun*
Feces are a **waste product** found in the **intestine**. They are also called stools or bowel movements. Feces are what is left of food after all the **nutrients** have been broken down, or **digested**, and absorbed into the body. They are formed in the large intestine and passed out through the **anus**. Normal feces are brown and soft.
Feces contain harmful bacteria, which is why it is important to wash one's hands after going to the toilet.
fecal *adjective*

feelings *noun*
Feelings are different moods, or states of mind. They are also called emotions. Love, hate, happiness, and sadness are all feelings. Some feelings have an effect on the body. Anxiety, fear, or excitement make the heart beat faster and breathing become more rapid. **Hormones** have an effect on feelings. During adolescence, the hormones are working hard to help a child grow into an adult. This may produce very strong feelings.
She was so angry, she gave way to her feelings and shouted.

female *adjective*
Female refers to girls and women and behavior usually associated with them. The opposite of female is **male**.
A high voice is a female characteristic.

femur *noun*
A femur is the **bone** that joins the **hip** to the **knee**. The femur, or thighbone, is the longest and one of the strongest bones in the body. Powerful **muscles** help the femur move.
The femoral artery runs down the thigh.
femoral *adjective*

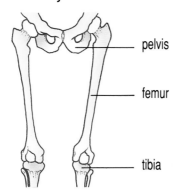

fertile *adjective*
Fertile describes a person who is able to have children. Fertile women have **ova** that can be fertilized by **sperm**. A fertile woman must also have a **uterus** that can carry a baby. Fertile men have sperm that are able to fertilize eggs. Women can be fertile from **puberty** to about 45 years of age. Men can be fertile from puberty until old age.
The tests showed that she was fertile and could have a baby.
fertility *noun*

fertilization *noun*
Fertilization describes what happens when a **sperm** meets an **ovum**. Fertilization is also called **conception**. The sperm and ovum join and form a bundle of **cells** called a zygote. This grows into an **embryo**, and then a **fetus**.
Fertilization can be done artificially in a laboratory.

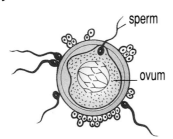

fetus *noun*
The human offspring is called a fetus from two months after **conception** until it is born. In the **uterus**, the fetus floats in **amniotic fluid** and receives its nourishment through the **umbilical cord**.
The doctor used an ultrasound scanner to examine the fetus.

fever *noun*
A fever is a rise in body **temperature**. When a person's temperature rises above the normal level of about 98.6°F, he or she has a fever. A person with a fever may feel hot and then cold and shivery. One may also feel tired and have a **headache**. Usually a symptom of an **infection**, fevers can be a sign of serious illness.
She stayed in bed suffering from a high fever.
feverish *adjective*

fiber *noun*
Fiber is the layer of tiny strands that makes up **cell** walls in plants. Vegetables, fruits, beans, and cereals all contain fiber. When it is eaten, fiber cannot be broken down, or **digested**. As it travels through the **large intestine**, it absorbs water and forms **feces**. People who do not eat enough fiber may suffer from **constipation**.
He ate plenty of fiber in his diet to stay healthy.
fibrous *adjective*

fibroid *noun*
A fibroid is a lump of **tissue** formed from tiny strands of fiber. Fibroids sometimes develop in the **uterus**. They are a harmless, or **benign**, growth and often cause no problems. However, large fibroids may cause cramps or heavy bleeding during **menstruation**. They may also stop a woman from having a child. Fibroids that cause problems can be removed by a surgical operation.
She recovered quickly after the fibroids were removed.

fibula   *noun*
A fibula is the long, thin **bone** that runs down the outside of the lower leg. The top end of the fibula joins the shinbone, or **tibia**, just below the knee. The bottom end forms the outer side of the ankle joint. **Muscles** attached to the fibula help the leg to move.
The boy fractured his fibula just above the ankle.

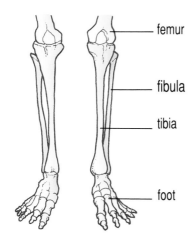

femur
fibula
tibia
foot

finger   *noun*
Fingers, or digits, are found at the end of each **hand**. Four of the fingers on each hand are made of three bones called **phalanges**. The two fingers called thumbs have only two phalanges. The bones of the fingers are joined by **joints** that act like hinges. **Tendons** along the fingers move the joints. These movements are controlled by muscles in the forearm. Many **nerve endings** make them very sensitive to touch.
We use our fingers to grip tools and in many other movements.

fingernail   *noun*
A fingernail is a piece of hard **tissue** at the end of each finger. It is made of a horny substance called **keratin** which is waterproof. The nail itself is not supplied with **blood** or **nerves**. It is dead tissue and does not hurt when it is cut. Serious illness may damage a person's fingernails.
Fingernails protect the fleshy ends of the fingers from injury.

first aid ▶ page 60

flex   *verb*
To flex is to bend a **joint** or tense a **muscle**. Joints allow people to flex their body.
She flexed her biceps muscle when she lifted the jug of water.
flexible   adjective

fluoride   *noun*
Fluoride is a chemical substance found naturally in soil and water. Fluoride helps **bones** and **teeth** to form and helps to prevent tooth decay, or **caries**. But taking too much fluoride can be harmful to teeth.
Fluoride is often added to water supplies and toothpaste to help keep people's teeth healthy.

follicle ▶ **hair follicle**

food   *noun*
Food is the name for all the substances that nourish the body. Food consists of plants and animals and can be arranged in four groups. These are the milk group, the meat group, the bread and cereal group, and the fruit and vegetable group. A healthy **diet** consists of a balance of these foods. Some people do not eat meat; they are called **vegetarians**. Food is measured in units of energy called **calories**.
Without food, we cannot live.

food poisoning   *noun*
Food poisoning is an illness that attacks the **digestive system** and causes **vomiting**, **diarrhea**, and stomach pains. Food poisoning is usually caused by eating food that contains harmful **bacteria**. Food that contains poisonous chemicals may also cause food poisoning. Some plants, such as some fungi, are very poisonous to humans and should never be eaten. People recover from most attacks of food poisoning after a day or so.
He took special fluids to treat his food poisoning.

first aid   *noun*

First aid is immediate treatment that is given to a person who is taken ill or has had an accident. First aid can save a person's life. It can also prevent a person's condition from getting worse. Someone should call for a doctor or other help as quickly as possible.
In the first aid course, he learned how to tie a sling for a broken arm.

Someone who feels faint should sit down, with the head between the knees.

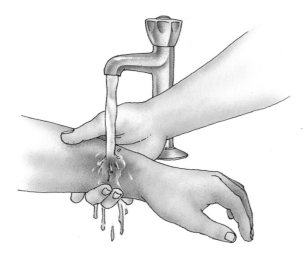

Some burns should be cooled under running water.

If someone is not breathing, artificial respiration should be given by a person with special training.

If poisoning is suspected, an ambulance should be called immediately.

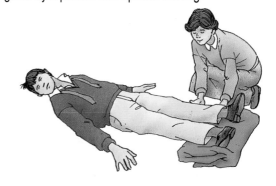

A person in shock should lie down, with the feet raised slightly. Tight clothing should be loosened.

foot (plural **feet**)   *noun*
A foot is a part of the body that lies at the
end of the lower leg. It is made up of 26
small **bones**. Each foot has a **heel**, an **arch**,
and five **toes**. The arch of the foot is
formed by five bones called the metatarsals
that join the ankle to the toes. The largest
bone in the foot is the heel bone, or
calcaneus.
*Feet are used for standing, walking, and
running.*

forceps   *plural noun*
Forceps are pincers used for holding and
seizing objects in surgical **operations**.
They used forceps to deliver the baby.

forehead   *noun*
A forehead is the part of a **face** above the
eyes. The forehead, or brow, runs from the
hairline to the **eyebrows**.
Her long hair fell down over her forehead.

foreskin   *noun*
The foreskin is a fold of skin that covers the
end of the penis. The foreskin can be pulled
back in boys after the age of about three
years. Before this, the foreskin is held in
place by fine strands of **tissue**. Cutting away
part or all of the foreskin is called
circumcision.
*It is important always to keep the foreskin
clean.*

fracture ▶ page 62

freckle   *noun*
A freckle is a small brown patch on the skin.
Freckles appear on some people after they
are exposed to sunlight. This is because the
body makes more of the pigment called
melanin to protect the skin from burning.
Fair-skinned people are more likely to have
freckles than dark-skinned people. Freckles
fade eventually if the skin is exposed to no
more sun.
*After a day in the sun, freckles appeared all
over her nose.*

fungus (plural **fungi**)   *noun*
A fungus is a plant. Some tiny fungi can live
and spread on humans, usually on the skin.
Fungi are sometimes breathed into the **lungs**
and develop into an illness. Fungal infections
include **athlete's foot** and **ringworm**.
*Fungicide is a substance that kills fungi and
can be used to treat some fungal infections.*

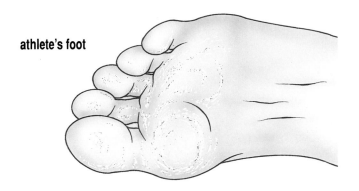

athlete's foot

funny bone ▶ **humerus**

fracture *noun*

A fracture is a broken **bone**. Fractures are one of the most common injuries that result from accidents. The treatment of a fracture is usually straightforward. A broken limb is often set in a **plaster cast** so that it cannot move until the break heals. The bones of older people are more brittle than those of younger people. They break more easily and take longer to heal.

The X-ray showed that he had a fracture of the tibia.

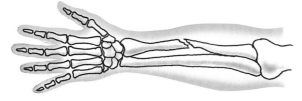

Simple fracture. A clean break.

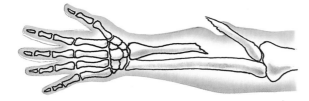

Open fracture. The bone pierces through the skin.

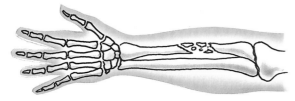

Comminuted fracture. The bone is shattered at the break.

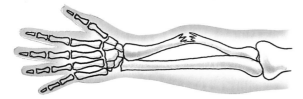

Greenstick fracture. The bone breaks only on one side. This kind of fracture is common among children.

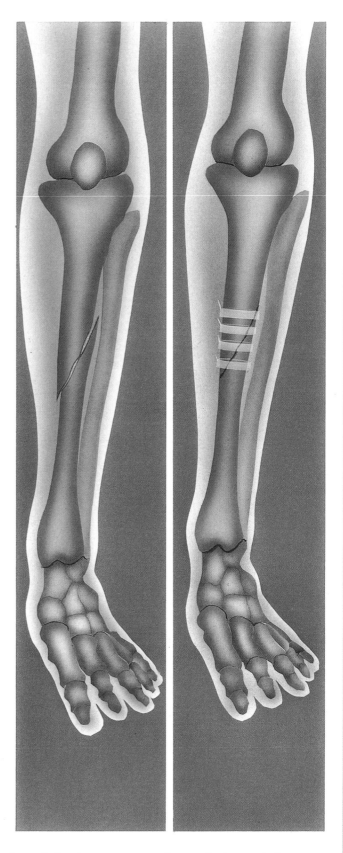

A metal pin, plate, screws, or wire may be inserted where a fracture is very difficult to treat.

gall bladder　*noun*

A gall bladder is an **organ** in the body that stores a digestive juice called **bile**. It is about four inches long and shaped like a pear. The gall bladder lies under the right side of the **liver** and it is attached to the liver and the **duodenum** by a tube called the **bile** duct. From the gall bladder, bile is passed along the bile duct to the **intestines**.
Some people develop small lumps or stones in their gall bladder.

gastric　*adjective*

Gastric describes anything to do with the **stomach**. Gastric juice is the **acid** liquid the stomach makes to break down, or **digest**, food. Gastric diseases are those that affect the stomach.
His gastric problems caused him to have indigestion.

gastroenteritis　*noun*

Gastroenteritis is an **inflammation** of the stomach and intestine. People with this illness have **diarrhea**, stomach pains, and **vomiting**. If the symptoms are severe, a person may suffer from loss of fluid, or **dehydration**. Dehydration can be dangerous in babies and children, and they need to be treated in the hospital. Gastroenteritis is caused by harmful **bacteria** in food, **viruses**, **allergies**, or poisons.
Someone with gastroenteritis should rest and drink plenty of fluids.

gene ▶ genetics

genetics ▶ page 64

generation　*noun*

Generation means a single stage in the history of a family or all the people born about the same time. Physical characteristics are passed from one generation to the next. Generations of people are counted in periods of about 30 years.
Her parents belong to a different generation than she does.

germ　*noun*

A germ is a tiny organism that can only be seen under a microscope. **Bacteria, viruses,** and **fungi** are all germs. Some germs are harmless, but others can cause **diseases** when they enter the body and start to grow in number, or multiply.
When he had a cold, he covered his mouth when he coughed so he wouldn't spread germs.

German measles ▶ rubella

gestation ▶ pregnancy

gingivitis　*noun*

Gingivitis is an **inflammation** of the **gums**. The gums become sore and swollen, and they bleed when the teeth are brushed. The inflammation is caused by **bacteria** in the mouth that form a hard, scaly substance called **plaque** at the base of each tooth. Plaque irritates the gums and causes the inflammation of gingivitis.
Gingivitis may result from not brushing the teeth properly.

gland　*noun*

A gland is an **organ** of the body. Glands make and store different kinds of fluid, such as **sweat** and **hormones**. There are two kinds of gland in the body. Exocrine glands pass fluids along tubes called **ducts**. **Endocrine glands** pass fluids directly into the **bloodstream**.
The lymph glands located in the neck and armpits are also called lymph nodes.
glandular　*adjective*.

genetics *noun*

Genetics is the study of how features are passed from parents to offspring through their **genes.** The **nucleus** of each human body cell contains 46 **chromosomes.** Every chromosome carries **genes** that contain **hereditary** information. Physical **characteristics**, some mental abilities, and hereditary disorders are inherited by children from their parents.

Genetics has helped scientists to produce useful medicines cheaply and easily.

Boy or girl

An egg fertilized by a sperm with an x-chromosome will become a girl.

Chromosomes decide a person's sex. The father produces two kinds of sperm. One kind has a special x-chromosome, and another has a y-chromosome. The mother's egg cell has only an x-chromosome.

An egg fertilized by a sperm with a y-chromosome will become a boy.

Strong and weak genes

Human body cells contain 23 pairs of chromosomes. One of each pair is inherited from the mother and one from the father. If a boy inherits a brown-eye gene from his mother and a blue-eye gene from his father, the boy will have brown eyes, because the brown-eye gene is stronger, or dominant. But the boy will still have a 'hidden' blue-eye gene. When he grows up and has children himself, he might pass on his blue-eye gene.

Growing cells

Chromosomes are made of a protein called DNA. Each chromosome carries about 1,000 genes that are strung together in a long, twisted chain. When body cells multiply, they divide in two. As this happens, the chain of chromosomes makes an exact copy of itself, one for each new cell. So each body cell contains exactly the same genetic information.

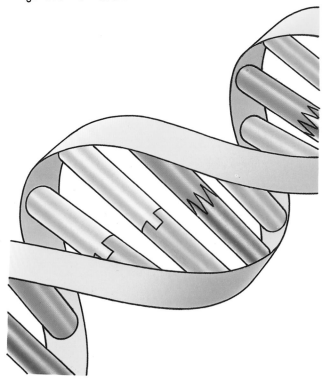

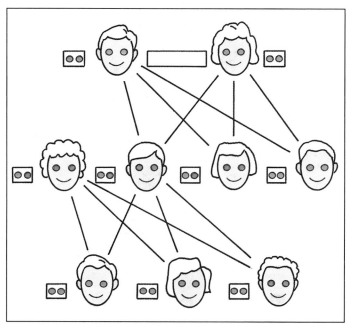

glaucoma *noun*
Glaucoma is a **disease** of the **eye**. It may
develop suddenly, or build up slowly.
Glaucoma is caused by fluid in the center of
the **eyeball** pressing against the back of the
eye and the **retina** becomes damaged.
Sudden, or **acute**, glaucoma causes pain in
the eye and vision is blurred. A person with
glaucoma is unable to see things around the
object they are looking at. This is called
tunnel vision.
Glaucoma can be helped by drugs which get
rid of the extra fluid.

glottis ► **larynx**

glucose *noun*
Glucose is a kind of sugar. It is found in most
foods that contain sugar and starch. People
need glucose for **energy**. Glucose is
absorbed straight into the **bloodstream** from
the **intestine**. The brain needs glucose in
order to function properly. **Hormones** in the
body balance the levels of glucose.
Glucose which is not used up as energy is
stored as fat.

goitre *noun*
A goitre is a swelling of the **thyroid gland**. It
is usually caused by a lack of iodine in the
diet. A goitre can also result when the
pituitary gland works too hard, or is
overactive.
A goitre can be treated by adding salt with
iodine to a person's diet.

gonad *noun*
A gonad is the organ that produces
reproductive cells. The male gonads are
called the **testes**, and the female gonads are
called the **ovaries**.
The gonads mature during adolescence.

gout *noun*
Gout is a sickness in which there is swelling
and pain in the joints, especially in the big
toe.
Gout is a hereditary disease.

graft *noun*
A graft is an **operation** to repair a part of the
body. Healthy **tissue** is taken from a different
part of the body, or another person. It is then
attached to the damaged area and left to
heal. Skin is the most common part of the
body used to make a graft, but grafts can
also be made from organs, such as hearts,
kidneys, and livers. Bones, muscles, tendons
and many other parts of the body as well as
artificial materials are also used as grafts.
A skin graft is a very useful treatment for
severe burns.

gray matter ► **cerebral cortex**

growth ► page 66

growth hormone *noun*
Growth hormone is a **hormone** released by
the **pituitary gland** that regulates normal
growth.
Sometimes children whose bodies don't
produce enough natural growth hormone can
be treated with a synthetic hormone.

gullet ► **esophagus**

gum *noun*
A gum is part of the **mouth**. Gums are the
pink, dense **tissue** in which **teeth** are buried.
A moist layer of **skin** covers the gums.
Teeth and gums should be brushed at least
once a day to keep them healthy.

gut ► **intestine**

gynecology *noun*
Gynecology is the study and treatment of
illnesses that are found only in girls and
women. Gynecology deals with
menstruation, as well as any problems to do
with the **breasts** and genitals.
There is a special gynecology unit in most
hospitals.

growth *noun*
1. Growth is an increase in size. It also means development. The growth of a human **embryo** into an adult takes many years. Most people stop growing when they are between 18 and 24 years old. Growth is controlled by a **hormone** in the **pituitary gland** of the brain.
Foods containing proteins, vitamins, and minerals are essential for healthy growth.
2. A lump in the body, or **tumor**, is sometimes called a growth.
The growth on her neck had to be surgically removed.

As a person grows, the body gets bigger in relation to the head.

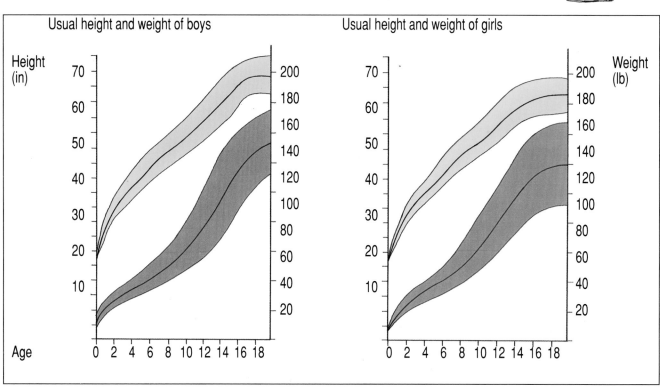

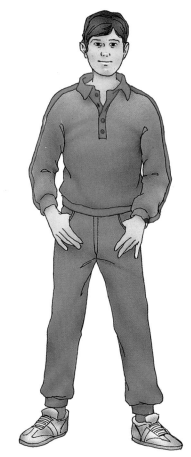

The pituitary gland in the brain produces the growth hormone. The hormone is released into the bloodstream and stimulates growth in the body.

Hormones produced by the thyroid influence cell growth.

Hormones produced by the pancreas also influence cell growth.

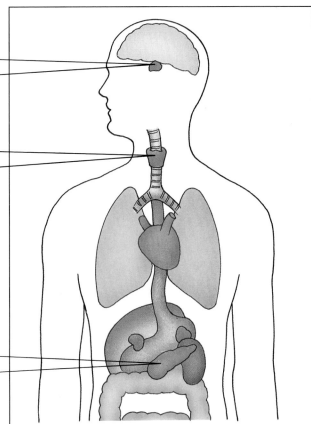

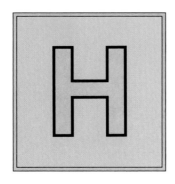

hair ► page 69

hair follicle   *noun*
A hair follicle is a tiny space under the **skin** that makes and feeds a **hair**. The root of a hair is planted at the bottom of the follicle. Oily fluid passes into the follicle from the **sebaceous gland** beside it. This helps the hair to grow. A tiny **muscle** attached to the follicle can make hairs stand on end.
Hair follicles stand up when a person is cold or afraid and cause goose pimples.

halitosis   *noun*
Halitosis is bad or unpleasant-smelling breath. It is usually caused by not cleaning the teeth and gums properly or it may be a sign of a throat, nose, or lung **infection**. Sometimes it is a symptom of other illnesses.
Halitosis can sometimes be cured by a change of diet.

hammer   *noun*
The hammer is one of the three tiny **bones** in the **middle ear**. The other two bones are called the **anvil** and the **stirrup**. Together, they are called the **ossicles**.
The hammer is a bone that helps in the process of hearing.

hand   *noun*
The hand is the end part of the arm. Each hand has five nails at the end of five fingers. The palm of each hand is formed by five bones called metacarpals, which join the wrist to the **fingers**. The whole hand has 27 bones and a web of **muscles** and **tendons**.
The hands can move in many different ways.

harelip   *noun*
A harelip is a congenital disorder in which the upper lip is split. There is sometimes also a split in the **palate**.
Harelip is treated surgically when the baby is about 10 weeks old.

hay fever   *noun*
Hay fever is an **allergy**. It is an unusual reaction to tiny particles in the air, such as dust, or pollen from plants. People with hay fever cough and sneeze, and have a runny, stuffy nose, and watering eyes. Hay fever is **hereditary**, which means it can be passed down in families. There are drugs that help the symptoms of hay fever.
She always suffers from hay fever in the hot weather.

head   *noun*
1. The head is the top part of the body. The head contains the **brain** and includes the **face**, **scalp**, and **ears**. It is formed by the bones of the **skull**.
The side of the head is called the temple.
2. A head is the rounded end of a **bone** which fits into another to form a **joint**.
The head of the femur fits into the pelvis.

headache   *noun*
A headache is a pain in the **head**, usually caused by muscle tension. Headaches can also be caused by an **infection**, a disorder of the **eye** or **ear**, or a head injury. Some headaches may be a **symptom** of an illness.
She took a painkiller to treat her headache.

heal   *verb*
Healing is the way the body mends itself when it is ill or injured. Some **cells** renew themselves to repair damage, such as when the skin is cut. Other cells fight **germs** and allow the body to recover from **infection**. The body's **immune system** is important in helping the body heal. **Medicines** and **operations** help heal the body.
The cut formed a scab, then healed completely within a few days.

hair *noun*

Hair is a part of the body that grows from the **skin**. Each hair is a fine thread of tough **protein** called **keratin**. Keratin cells are not alive. Hair grows all over the body except for the palms of the hands and the soles of the feet. The thickest area of hair grows from the **head**. Hairs grow, fall out and are replaced by new ones all the time. Hairs on the head last from two to five years before they are shed. Hair protects the body from dust and dirt and helps to keep it warm.

There are about 100,000 hairs on a human head.

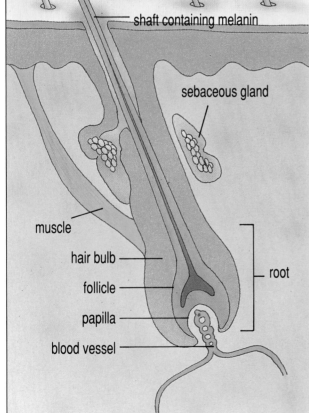

Hair color is decided by a pigment called melanin in the hair shaft. Older people's hair often turns grey or white because melanin stops being produced.

Hair texture depends on the shape of the hair follicles.

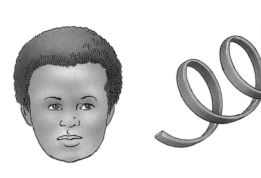

Flat hairs are curly.

Oval hairs are wavy.

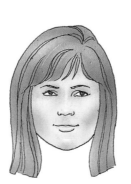

Round hairs are straight.

health *noun*

Health is the condition of body and mind.
People with good health are fit and well.
People with bad health may be suffering
from some kind of illness.
Everyone feels better if their health is good.

Eating a balanced diet keeps people healthy.

Exercise strengthens the muscles and improves breathing
and blood circulation.

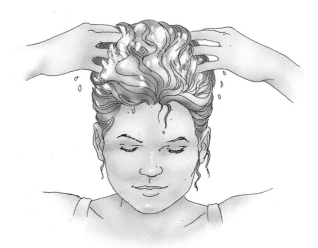

Keeping clean controls the growth of harmful bacteria.

Good personal relationships are important.

People who do not get enough sleep do not function well.

health ► page 70

hearing *noun*
Hearing is being able to detect sound. The **ear** is the organ of hearing. A person who can't hear is suffering from **deafness**.
A person who cannot hear well may use a hearing aid.

heart ► page 72

heartbeat *noun*
A heartbeat is the pumping action of the **heart**. A heartbeat is felt every time the muscles of the heart contract to push **blood** around the body. The heart beats about 72 times a minute in a resting adult. Heatbeats can be felt as a throb of pressure, or **pulse**, in the **arteries** of the wrist and neck.
The heartbeat of a young child is faster than that of an adult.

heart disease *noun*
Heart disease is any disorder that affects the **heart**. Any kind of heart disease causes problems with the **circulation** of **blood**. **Operations** can cure some kinds of heart disease, and other kinds can be treated with **drugs**. **Angina** and **hypertension** are examples of heart disease. Coronary heart disease occurs when the heart muscle does not get enough blood.
Eating less fat, exercising, and not smoking cut down the risk of heart disease.

heat *noun*
Extreme heat can cause illness. If the body becomes too hot, a person may have heat exhaustion or heatstroke. He or she may sweat and shiver, feel dizzy, nauseous, and have a headache because the body is unable to control its temperature. A person may also develop dry, hot skin and become very confused. **Shock**, **convulsions**, **coma**, and even death may follow without emergency treatment.
People with heat exhaustion should rest quietly in a cool place, and drink some water.

heel *noun*
A heel is the rear end of the foot. It is formed by the heel bone, or **calcaneus**, resting on a thick pad of skin. Heels bear the full weight of the body and act as shock absorbers.
When walking, one usually puts the heel down first.

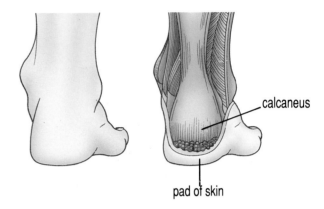

calcaneus

pad of skin

hemoglobin *noun*
Hemoglobin is the substance in **red blood cells** that gives them their color. Its function is to carry **oxygen** from the **lungs** to the rest of the body.
Sickle-cell anemia is a disease caused by abnormal hemoglobin.

hemorrhage *noun*
A hemorrhage is heavy **bleeding** from a damaged **blood vessel**. This can happen deep inside or near the skin. A hemorrhage is dangerous and must be stopped as quickly as possible.
A hemorrhage sometimes results in loss of large amounts of blood.

hemorrhoids *noun*
Hemorrhoids are a disorder of the **anus** and **rectum**. They are a bunch of swollen veins that bulge either inside, or just outside, the anus. They cause pain, burning, and itching, and they may bleed when **feces** are passed. **Constipation** or **pregnancy** sometimes cause hemorrhoids, but they can appear and disappear at any age.
Hemorrhoids are sometimes also known as piles.

heart *noun*

The heart is an organ made of **muscle**. It is about the size of a clenched fist, and lies between the **lungs**. The heart is divided into four sections, or **chambers**. These are the left and right **atrium**, and the left and right **ventricle**. The heart pumps **blood** around the circulatory system. Blood carries essential **oxygen** and **nutrients** to each **cell** in the body. The body cannot live for more than about five minutes if the heart stops completely.

The heart of an adult beats about 70 times a minute.

Valves in the heart make sure the blood flows the correct way. Many large veins also have valves.

valve open

valve closed

pulmonary artery carries blood to lungs

vena cava carries blood from the body's cells

aorta carries blood to the body's cells

pulmonary veins carry blood from lungs

left atrium

valve

left ventricle

right atrium   right ventricle

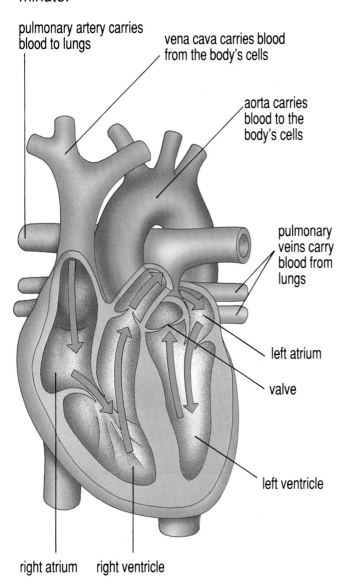

How the heart works

The heart relaxes. Blood flows in to both atria from the veins.

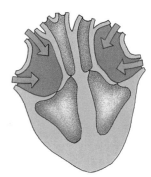

The atria contract, and push blood through the valves into the ventricles.

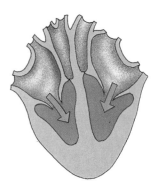

The ventricles contract, pushing open the semilunar valves. Blood flows into the arteries. This contraction is felt as a heartbeat.

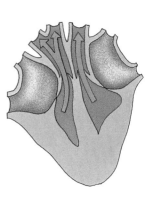

hepatitis   *noun*

Hepatitis is an **inflammation** of the **liver**. Sometimes **jaundice** also develops, along with weakness and **nausea**. Hepatitis may last for weeks or months. It is usually caused by one of four kinds of **infectious virus**, called A, B, C, and D. Type A is caught from water or food that has been contaminated with **feces** or **urine**. The other types are caught by contact with other body fluids, such as **blood**.
Hepatitis sometimes causes liver failure that can be fatal.

heredity   *noun*

Heredity is how parents pass on **characteristics** to their children. Traits like appearance and intelligence are inherited. Sometimes a tendency toward a certain illness is also hereditary. A feature that can be traced back through the family is described as hereditary.
Genetics is the study of heredity.
hereditary   *adjective*

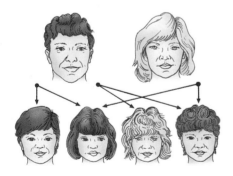

herpes   *noun*

Herpes is a skin **infection** caused by a **virus**. A small blister appears and then breaks into a sore. The sore then dries up, heals and forms a **scab**. Herpes around the mouth and nose are usually called cold sores because they often appear with a cold. Another kind of herpes appears on the genitals. Both kinds of herpes tend to come back again and again.
Sometimes a long time passes between outbreaks of herpes, but there is no cure.

hiccup   *noun*

A hiccup is a short breath of air sucked in very suddenly when the **diaphragm** muscle in the stomach tightens in a spasm. Air is pulled in and hits the **epiglottis** so quickly it is like banging a tiny drum. This causes the 'hic' noise of a hiccup. Hiccups can be hard to get rid of.
An upset stomach or stress are two causes of hiccups.

hinge joint ► joint

hip   *noun*

A hip is a bone found on each side of the **pelvis**, where the legs join the rest of the body. The **femur** is attached to the pelvis by a ball and socket **joint**. Strong ligaments support the hip joint. The pelvis is formed from the two hipbones and the lower spine.
Women usually have wider hips than men, which helps them during childbirth.

HIV   *noun*

HIV is the **virus** that causes **AIDS**. HIV stands for Human Immunodeficiency Virus. It slowly attacks the body's defense against illness, or the **immune system**. HIV is caught by coming into contact with infected body fluids, such as blood or semen. Any sexual contact carries the risk of HIV infection. People with HIV may not feel ill or know they are carrying the virus for many years before AIDS develops. A blood test can show if a person is infected.
There is no known cure for the HIV infection though a lot of research is being done.

hives   *noun*

Hives are red, painful swellings on the **skin**. They are usually caused by an **allergic** reaction to a drug or an insect bite. Hives can also be an allergic reaction to certain foods, such as shellfish or eggs. They can appear anywhere on the body and can last a few days. There are **drugs** that ease the **symptoms** of hives.
The bee sting gave her hives.

hygiene   *noun*

Hygiene is a way of staying healthy by keeping clean. Bodies need to be washed and teeth brushed to stop **bacteria** building up. Most bacteria on the body are harmless, but some kinds, such as in **feces**, can cause illness. It is important always to wash the hands after using the toilet and before touching food.

Public hygiene is also very important in keeping people healthy. It involves steps taken by governments and voluntary health organizations to improve the general health of a community. Sewage systems and immunization programmes are part of public hygiene.

Personal hygiene such as washing your hands regularly is as important as public hygiene.

Brushing teeth keeps them healthy. Without regular brushing, bacteria in the mouth combine with food particles and acid to form plaque. Plaque causes tooth decay and gum disease.

Minor wounds should be washed carefully then covered with a sterile dressing to stop bacteria getting into the cut and causing an infection.

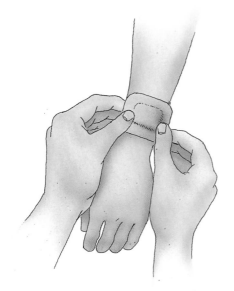

Washing hands destroys harmful bacteria, which could cause illness.

Flies cause disease by spreading bacteria. Food should be covered or kept in the refrigerator to prevent flies from coming into contact with it.

Careful preparation of food prevents growth of bacteria. Rules of hygiene such as keeping hands clean and touching prepared food as little as possible must be followed.

Careful control of the way food is processed makes sure that it is safe to eat by destroying any bacteria that may be present.

Sewage systems process waste hygienically, to keep harmful bacteria away from public places.

homeopathy   *noun*
Homeopathy is a kind of **alternative medicine**. It is a way of treating illness with small amounts of certain medicines, which are mostly made of herbs mixed with alcohol and diluted with water.
Homeopathy was introduced by Samuel Hahnemann in about 1800.

hookworm   *noun*
A hookworm is a worm that is usually found in tropical countries. Hookworms get into the body through the **skin**, usually on bare feet. They travel through the bloodstream to the lungs, then to the throat, and find their way to the **small intestine**, where they suck blood for food and grow up to about half an inch long.
People with hookworm may feel sick, have diarrhea and experience stomach pain.

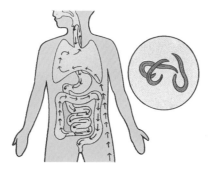

hormone   *noun*
A hormone is a chemical substance made in the body. **Organs** such as the **endocrine glands** make different kinds of hormones, which help the body develop and work properly.
Males and females have different amounts of hormones.

hospice   *noun*
Hospice is a place that cares for dying people. Hospice is also a kind of medical care for people who are close to **death**. People with serious illnesses that cannot be cured and some elderly people need special care. Hospice care gives nursing and support for the patients, their family, and friends.
She visited her aunt at the hospice.

hospital   *noun*
A hospital is where people go to hospitals to have medical treatment they cannot have at home, or through their family doctor. **Operations**, for example, are performed in the hospital. Babies are also usually born there.
Hospitals deal with all kinds of disorders of the body.

host   *noun*
A host is a person whose body provides food and a home for another animal, such as a **tapeworm**.
Animals that exist in or on living hosts are called parasites.

human   *noun*
A human is a person. Humans are mammals, or animals with warm blood, that feed their offspring with breast milk. Humans are the most powerful species on Earth, since we control and use most other life forms, and even change the planet itself.
Young humans need to be cared for longer than any other young animal.

humerus   *noun*
A humerus is the **bone** of the upper arm that joins the shoulder to the elbow. The lower end of the humerus is called sometimes the funny bone. Hitting the back of the elbow often strikes the ulnar nerve on the funny bone, which causes a tingling pain that shoots up and down the arm.
It was not funny when the boy broke his humerus.

hunger   *noun*
Hunger is the feeling of wanting to eat food. People suffering from hunger sometimes have a pain in the upper part of the **abdomen**, and the **stomach** may gurgle and rumble. The sight or smell of food makes saliva rush to the mouth of a hungry person. Hunger is controlled in a part of the brain called the **hypothalamus**.
Hunger made him feel empty and weak.

hygiene ► page 74

hypertension *noun*
Hypertension is high **blood pressure**. Often there are no symptoms, but untreated hypertension increases the risk of heart disease, stroke, and kidney disease. Being overweight, eating too much salt, drinking too much alcohol, and suffering **stress** may all contribute to hypertension.
Hypertension can damage the heart, blood vessels, and kidneys unless it is treated.

hypothalamus *noun*
The hypothalamus is part of the **brain** that links the **endocrine system** and the **nervous system** in the brain stem. It controls the activity of the **pituitary gland**. The hypothalamus lies below the **thalamus** and above the **pituitary gland**.
The hypothalamus controls appetite, thirst, and body temperature.

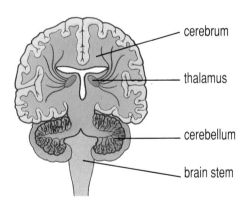

- cerebrum
- thalamus
- cerebellum
- brain stem

hypothermia *noun*
Hypothermia is an illness that occurs when the **temperature** of the body drops far below normal. All the **organs** in the body slow down and it is difficult to move. The person becomes confused and cannot talk properly. People with hypothermia may not realize they are in danger. They may then become unconscious, fall into a **coma**, and die.
People who are not dressed for cold weather are at risk of hypothermia.

ileum *noun*
The ileum is the lowest part of the **small intestine**. In an adult, it is about 12 feet long. The ileum runs from the middle part of the small intestine, or jejunum, to the start of the **large intestine**. Digested food is absorbed into the blood in the ileum.
Undigested food passes from the ileum into the large intestine.

ilium (plural ilia) *noun*
The ilium is a bone in the **pelvis**. There are two ilia, which are the largest upper parts of the hipbone on each side. The ilia are fused to two other bones called the **pubis** and the **ischium**.
Strong muscles in the upper legs and buttocks are attached to the ilia.

illness *noun*
An illness is a sickness or **disease**. It is a state of being unwell in the body or mind. An illness may be mild or serious, have a name or be unknown.
Her illness was difficult to diagnose.

immature *adjective*
Immature describes someone who is not fully grown. An immature person is not **adult**. Immature can also describe someone's personality and behavior. The opposite of immature is **mature**.
The baby held onto the chair because his muscles were too immature for him to stand alone.
immaturity *noun*

immune system ► page 78

77

immune system   *noun*

The immune system is the body's defense against **illness**. The main parts of the system are white **blood cells** which are made in the **bone marrow**, **lymph nodes**, and **spleen**. When harmful **bacteria** or **viruses** enter the body, the white blood cells go to the site of the infection or injury. Some white cells called phagocytes eat the bacteria. Others called lymphocytes make **antibodies** which help to fight the infection.
The immune system prevents illness by developing a resistance to some germs.

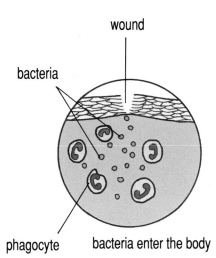

bacteria · wound · phagocyte · bacteria enter the body

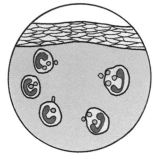

phagocytes crowd round the bacteria

phagocytes surround the bacteria and destroy them

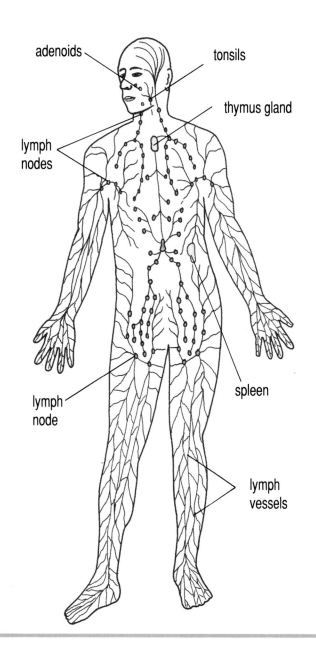

adenoids · tonsils · thymus gland · lymph nodes · spleen · lymph node · lymph vessels

Lymph is produced in the adenoids, the tonsils, the thymus gland, the spleen and the lymph nodes. Lymph circulates around the body through thin-walled vessels.

The body needs extra lymphocytes to fight an infection. So lymph nodes in the neck, armpits and groin swell up as they produce more lymphocytes.

immunity   *noun*

Immunity means protection from a specific disease. After a person has some illnesses, the white **blood cells** in the **immune system** are able to fight off an illness if it comes back. Because of this, many diseases, such as mononucleosis, can be caught only once. People also have immunity to certain diseases, such as smallpox, after they are given a **vaccination**. Babies receive some immunity from their mothers, passed across the **placenta** and in **colostrum** after birth.
There is no immunity to the common cold.

immunization   *noun*

Immunization helps the body fight off **infections** through **vaccinations**. The medicines used for immunization are given in a course of injections, or by mouth. The immunization of babies and children protects them against many diseases, such as **measles** and **mumps**.
Whooping cough can be prevented by immunization.

impetigo   *noun*

Impetigo is a skin **disease** that starts as a red patch and turns into small blisters. The blisters break and form crusty, yellow sores that ooze and spread over the body. Impetigo is caused by **bacteria**. It can develop from another skin disease, such as **eczema**. Impetigo is very **contagious**, or easy to catch, especially between children.
Antibiotic creams and drugs help to clear up impetigo.

implant   *noun*

An implant is something placed in or under the skin. This may be **tissue** from another part of the body, or a **drug**. It can sometimes be a pellet filled with a **hormone**, or a tube that feeds a substance into the body.
The pacemaker was an implant in the man's chest.

incisor ► tooth

incubator   *noun*

1. An incubator is a piece of hospital equipment. It is a special container for babies that are born very small, or sick. The incubator is a clear box that protects the baby from **infection** and keeps it warm. The air inside has the ideal mixture of moisture and oxygen for a newborn baby.
The premature baby was placed in an incubator.
2. Other kinds of incubators are used in medical tests.
The incubator provided the right mixture of air, moisture, and warmth to grow bacteria.

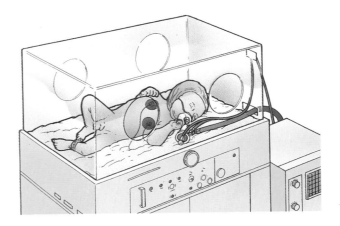

indigestion   *noun*

Indigestion is not being able to digest food properly. **Symptoms** may be **stomach** pain and **nausea**. Indigestion may also cause a burning pain in the chest. This kind of pain, called heartburn, is caused when acid in the stomach rises up into the **esophagus**. Indigestion may occasionally be a symptom of a more serious illness.
Indigestion is most often caused by eating too much too fast.

infection   *noun*

An infection is an illness that is caused by **germs** entering the body. **Viruses**, **bacteria**, and **worms** all cause infections. Germs can be breathed in, taken in food or water, or passed through the skin. Most infections can be treated with drugs called **antibiotics**.
People and animals can pass on infections.

infectious disease *noun*
An infectious **disease** is an **illness** that can be passed from one person to another. There are cures or **vaccines** for many infectious diseases, such as **diptheria**, **measles**, and **mumps**.
The common cold is an example of an infectious disease.

infertility *noun*
Infertility means not being able to have children. Sometimes infertility occurs because a woman's **ovaries** or **uterus** are not working properly. It may be caused by the man not making enough, or the right kind, of **sperm**. Often a cause cannot be found. Infertility may be either temporary or permanent.
Some kinds of infertility can be treated.
infertile *adjective*

inflammation *noun*
Inflammation is the reaction of the body to an **injury** or **disease.** The part of the body affected by inflammation becomes painful, red, and swollen.
Inflammation disappears as the body starts to heal.

inflammation of an
injured finger

influenza *noun*
Influenza is an **infectious disease** caused by a **virus.** After catching influenza, a person will feel shivery and sick. A headache, high temperature, and sore throat develop. People with influenza feel weak, their **muscles** and **joints** ache and they have a dry, painful cough.
Influenza usually lasts about five days, but a person may feel tired for a while afterward.

inhale *verb*
To inhale is to breathe in. Some illnesses can be treated by inhaling certain **drugs** or gases which make it easier for a person to breathe. People with **asthma** often carry an inhaler. This is a small container that puffs a mist of drugs into the mouth to be inhaled.
He inhaled the medicine once a day.
inhalation *noun*

injection *noun*
An injection is a way of putting fluid into the body by using a needle attached to a tube of fluid called a syringe. Injections can be made into the **skin**, or through the skin and into **muscle** or a **vein.** They can also be made into a **joint** or around the **nerves** of the **spinal cord**.
Some diabetics give themselves injections of insulin daily.
inject verb

inner ear *noun*
The inner ear is the innermost part of the **ear**. It sends to the brain messages concerning **hearing** and **balance**. The **cochlea** in the inner ear is a fluid-filled tube, coiled like a snail shell, that passes impulses to the **auditory** nerve. The inner ear also has three more tubes called the **semi-circular canals**. Fluid in these tubes moves as the head moves. This information is sent to the brain, telling it about the position of the body.
The inner ear helps people to keep their balance.

inoculation ▶ **vaccination**

insomnia   *noun*
Insomnia is difficulty in sleeping. There are many different causes of insomnia, such as illness, pain, heat, noise, and depression.
Anxiety about exams sometimes causes insomnia.

instinct   *noun*
Instinct is a kind of **behavior** that is not learned. It is an action that a person or animal does without thinking, such as holding out the arms to break a fall. Instinct helps people survive when some kind of danger threatens.
Newborn babies turn their head toward the breast and suck by instinct.
instinctive   *adjective*

insulation   *noun*
Insulation is protection. The outer layers of **skin** and **fat** act as insulation for the rest of the body to hold in heat and keep the body at the right **temperature.** The outer layers of skin also prevent harmful substances or objects from entering the body and damaging the **organs**.
A person does not need to be overweight to have enough insulation from the cold.
insulate   *verb*

insulin   *noun*
Insulin is a **hormone** produced in the **pancreas** and released into the **bloodstream.** It controls the levels of blood sugar, or **glucose**, in the blood.
People develop an illness called diabetes if their body does not make enough insulin.

intellect   *noun*
The intellect is the thinking power of the **mind**. The intellect helps people to reason, understand, and remember. Teaching the intellect builds **intelligence**.
He used intellect, not strength, to solve the problem.
intellectual   *adjective*

intelligence   *noun*
Intelligence is the skills and knowledge of the **intellect**. It can be measured in a test called an IQ, which stands for Intelligence Quotient. IQ tests ask a person to solve problems and answer questions. The person's scores are then compared with the scores of other people of the same age.
Some people feel the IQ test isn't an adequate measure of intelligence.

intensive care   *noun*
Intensive care is a certain kind of care for very ill people in **hospitals**. An intensive care unit has special equipment and more doctors and nurses than other hospital departments. The equipment includes a life-support system. This keeps people alive if they are in a **coma** and unable to breathe on their own.
He was in intensive care for a week after the operation.

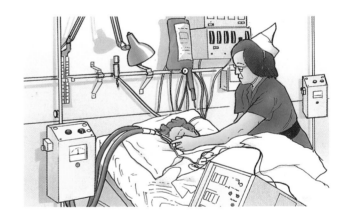

intestine   *noun*
The intestine is a long tube that lies coiled in the **abdomen**. It is also called the gut or the bowel. Food from the **stomach** passes through the intestine, where it is broken down, or **digested**. The **nutrients** from the food are absorbed into the body through the walls of the intestine, until only the waste matter, or **feces**, is left behind. The intestine is divided into two parts called the **small intestine** and the **large intestine**.
The intestine is about 25 feet long.

81

involuntary system *noun*
The involuntary system consists of the muscles that move without a person having to think about it. The muscles that control **blood vessels**, the **intestine**, and the **stomach** are all involuntary muscles. The **heart** is also part of the involuntary system. It beats through every minute of a person's life, even during sleep.
People don't usually control the muscles of the involuntary system.

iris *noun*
An iris is the part of an **eye** in front of the **lens** and behind the **cornea**. It is the ring around the **pupil** that gives the eye its color. Muscles in the iris control how much light passes through the pupil. In dim light, the iris becomes smaller, or contracts. This makes the pupil larger and able to take in as much light as it can. In bright light, the iris grows bigger. This makes the pupil smaller so less light is let into the eye.
It is the iris, not the pupil, that moves.

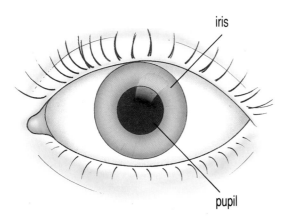

iron *noun*
Iron is an element. It is a metal that the body needs to stay healthy. Iron is found in foods such as eggs and lean meat, especially liver. The body stores iron in a part of the blood called **hemoglobin**. If people do not have enough iron in their blood, they develop an illness called **anemia**.
Pregnant women need extra iron to stay healthy.

ischium (plural ischia) *noun*
An ischium is one of two bones in the **pelvis**. There is one ischium on each lower side of the hipbone. The ischia join together to form an empty circle of bone with two loops at the bottom. The lower ends of these loops are what the body rests on while sitting. The ischia are joined, or fused, to two other parts of the hipbone called the **pubis** and the **ilium**.
His ischium was fractured in the car accident.

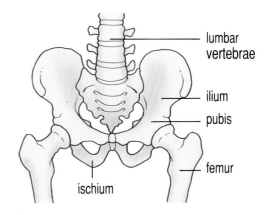

itch *noun*
An itch is a tickly feeling on the **skin** that makes people want to scratch it. Strong itches burn and tingle and feel uncomfortable. Scratching these kinds of itches may break the skin and make it sore. Dry skin, an **infection**, or an **allergy** can cause an itch. Nearly all scabs, spots, and rashes tend to itch.
Hay fever can make the eyes itch.

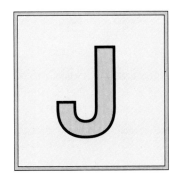

jaundice   *noun*

Jaundice occurs when the skin, eyeballs, and urine become unusually yellow. This can be a sign that the **liver** or **gall bladder** is not working properly. It may also be a **symptom** of other kinds of illnesses. Newborn babies often have mild jaundice for a few days but this kind is usually harmless and soon disappears.

As he recovered from jaundice, the yellow color of his eyeballs faded.

jaw   *noun*

A jaw is part of a **face**. The lower jaw runs from beneath each ear to the chin, forming the lower part of the face and mouth. The upper jaw forms the roof of the mouth and the holes that open out to the nose. It runs up to the bottom edge of the eye sockets and is joined each side to the cheekbones of the skull. Both jaws are made of bone and are called the **jawbones**.

She clenched her jaw so hard that her teeth ached.

jawbone   *noun*

The two jawbones are parts of the **face** in which the **teeth** are set. The upper jaw is made of two bones joined, or fused, together at the front. They are called **maxillae.** The upper jawbone is attached to the rest of the skull and does not move. The lower jawbone is made of two bones fused together at the front to form the chin. These are called **mandibles**. The upper and lower jawbone are joined together by a hinge **joint** under each ear. Strong muscles in the cheeks move the lower jawbone.

The lower jawbone is connected to the temple by ligaments.

jejunum   *noun*

A jejunum is a tube inside the body in the middle part of the **small intestine**. The jejunum is about four feet long and joins the other two parts of the small intestine, the **duodenum** and the **ileum**. Juices from the walls of the jejunum help to break down, or **digest**, food before it is passed on through the body.

The jejunum is important for digestion.

joint   ▶ page 84

joint ▶ page 84

jugular vein   *noun*

The jugular vein is a **blood vessel** in the neck and head. Two main jugular veins carry blood from the head back to the heart.

A jugular vein runs down each side of the neck.

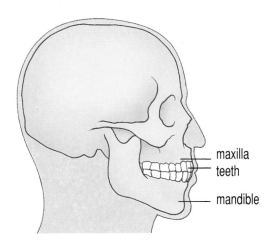

maxilla
teeth
mandible

joint *noun*

A joint is the place where two or more **bones** meet. Joints are held in place by strong, stretchy strips of **connective tissue**. These are called **tendons** and **ligaments**. If a joint twists too far, the ligaments may tear, causing a sprain. A joint that is pulled out of place is **dislocated**.
Her joints became stiff with arthritis.

A smooth layer of cartilage covers the ends of bones that move over each other. A liquid called synovial fluid helps the joints to move smoothly.

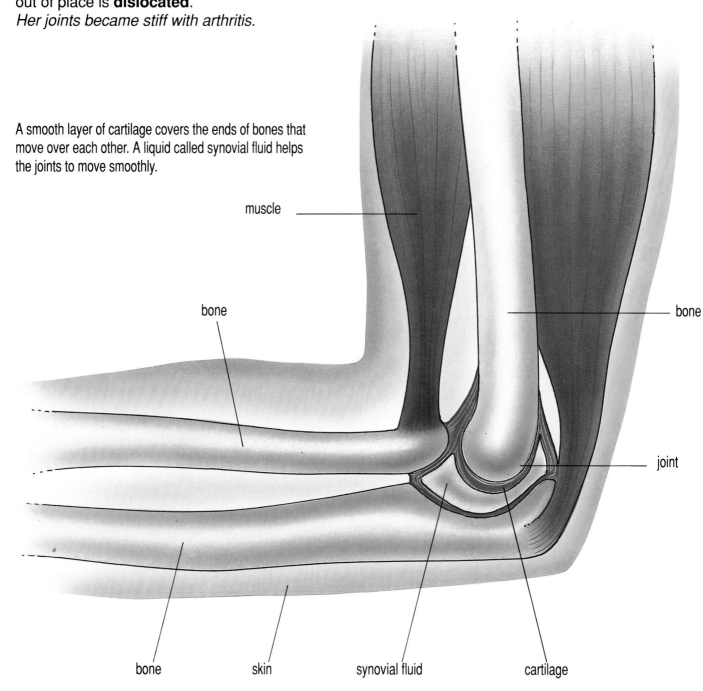

muscle

bone

bone

joint

bone   skin   synovial fluid   cartilage

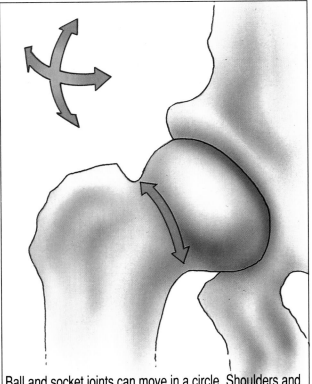

Ball and socket joints can move in a circle. Shoulders and hips have ball and socket joints.

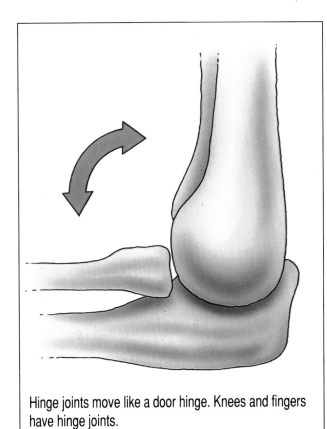

Hinge joints move like a door hinge. Knees and fingers have hinge joints.

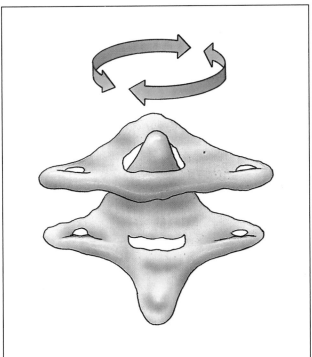

Pivot joints allow a rotating movement. The elbow and the first two vertebrae in the spine form pivot joints.

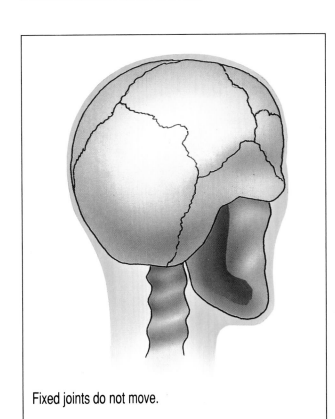

Fixed joints do not move.

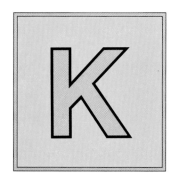

keratin   *noun*
Keratin is a tough substance made of
protein. It is found in the outer layer of the
skin and makes it waterproof. Keratin builds
up where the skin wears away the most,
such as the hands and feet. Nails, teeth, and
hair also contain keratin.
There are no nerves or blood vessels in
keratin.

kidney ▶ page 87

kidney machine ▶ **dialysis**

knee   *noun*
A knee is the **joint** of the **leg** that joins the
upper leg to the lower leg. Knees work like a
hinge and allow the legs to bend in half. The
front of each knee is covered by a small plate
of bone called the **kneecap** or patella. Strong
ligaments on either side of the knee and
inside the joint help keep it from becoming
dislocated.
The knee has to be strong enough to support
the weight of the whole body.

knee-jerk test ▶ **reflex**

kneecap   *noun*
A kneecap, or patella, is a small, disk-shaped
bone in front of the knee. It is in the middle of
the **tendon** that joins the thighbone, or
femur, to the shinbone, or **tibia**. The inside
of the kneecap is covered with **cartilage**, and
forms part of the **joint** that allows the leg to
bend.
The cartilage of his kneecap was damaged,
which made walking painful.

kwashiorkor   *noun*
Kwashiorkor is an illness found in children
who do not have enough food to eat. The
child develops a swollen stomach and feet
and the skin becomes dry, pale, and scaly.
Children with kwashiorkor cannot grow
properly. Without treatment their body
becomes very thin and the skin shrinks in
wrinkles over the bones.
Many children suffer from kwashiorkor during
a famine.

kidney   *noun*

A kidney is one of two **organs** in the body. The kidneys are about four inches long and lie on each side of the **spine** at the back of the abdomen. They filter the **blood** and keep it clean. The kidneys also collect water the body does not need. The water and waste material filtered by the kidneys form a yellow liquid called **urine**.

A person can live with only one kidney.

A filtering unit

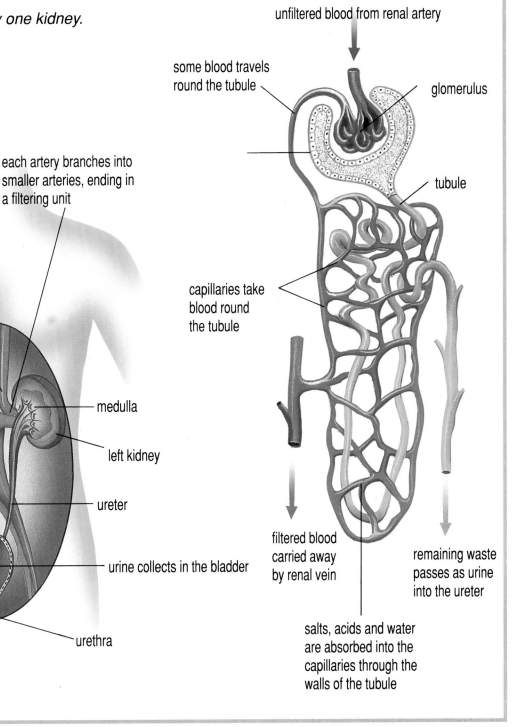

unfiltered blood from renal artery

some blood travels round the tubule

glomerulus

tubule

capillaries take blood round the tubule

filtered blood carried away by renal vein

remaining waste passes as urine into the ureter

salts, acids and water are absorbed into the capillaries through the walls of the tubule

blood flows into the kidneys through the renal artery

each artery branches into smaller arteries, ending in a filtering unit

adrenal gland

right kidney

artery

vein

medulla

left kidney

ureter

urine collects in the bladder

urethra

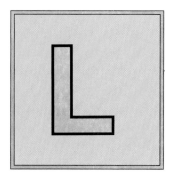

labia   *plural noun*

The labia are part of the outer sexual organs, or **vulva**, of a female. The labia are long folds of skin arranged in two pairs, one inside the other. The outer labia fold partly over the inner labia and surround the opening of the **vagina**. The inner labia help to protect the **clitoris** and the opening of the **urethra**.
During puberty, the outer labia grow a covering of pubic hair.

lacrimal gland   noun

A lacrimal gland is one of the two **glands**, one above each eye, that produce tears.
The muscle around the lacrimal glands tightened, and his eye filled with tears.

lactose   *noun*

Lactose is a kind of sugar found in milk. Some people are unable to **digest** lactose, which gives them stomach pain and **diarrhea**. People who react in this way to lactose cannot drink milk or eat food made with milk, such as butter, cheese, and cream.
She cannot eat dairy products because she cannot digest lactose.

laparoscopy   *noun*

A laparoscopy is a look inside the **abdomen**. This is done by a doctor with a lighted tube called a laparoscope. The tube is slipped into a small cut in the skin beside the **navel**. A doctor can look at the liver, intestine, bladder, uterus, and ovaries by carrying out a laparoscopy.
During the laparoscopy, the doctor found a problem with the man's liver.

large intestine   *noun*

The large intestine is joined to the **small intestine** and runs down to the opening of the **anus**. It is about five feet long. The three sections of the large intestine are the **cecum**, **colon**, and **rectum**. Water is taken in, or **absorbed**, from digested food in the large intestine. The waste left behind is passed out through the anus as **feces**.
Colitis is inflammation of the large intestine.

larynx   *noun*

The larynx is a part of the **throat**. The larynx reaches from the root of the tongue at the back of the mouth, down to the opening of the **trachea**, the airway to the **lungs**. The **vocal cords** inside the larynx help people make sounds.
When he reached puberty, his larynx grew bigger and his voice became deeper.

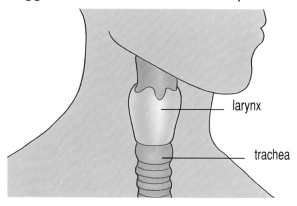

leg   noun

A leg is the lower **limb** of the body. The two legs are joined to the **pelvis** by the hip **joints**, and end in the **feet**. Strong **muscles** attached to the leg bones help them move.
The legs bend at the hips and knees.

lens   *noun*

A lens is part of an **eye**. It is the soft, clear disk that lies behind the **cornea** and the **iris**. Light is focused through the lens before it passes to the retina at the back of the eye. Muscles change the shape of the lens to focus at a long or a short distance.
A cataract causes the lens of the eye to become cloudy.

leprosy *noun*
Leprosy is a **disease** found in tropical areas. It develops slowly, attacking the skin and nerve endings. Patches of skin change color, become thicker, and lose all sense of feeling. In the worst form of leprosy, the skin develops lumps and open sores. Leprosy is caused by **bacteria**. It is infectious, but not highly contagious.
Leprosy can be treated with drugs.

leukemia noun
Leukemia is a **disease** of the **white blood cells**. It is a kind of **cancer** that starts in the **bone marrow**, where blood is made. White blood cells are part of the body's defense, or **immune system**. Some kinds of leukemia develop suddenly, but others develop slowly over a number of years. Symptoms of leukemia include weakness, **anemia**, bruising under the skin, and **nosebleeds**.
The girl with leukemia had a bone marrow transplant.

leukocyte ► white blood cell

lice (singular **louse**) *plural noun*
Lice are tiny insects that live on mammals. Head lice are easy to catch from another person. They climb onto a head and lay their eggs on hairs. Head lice make the head itch. Medicated shampoos and lotions get rid of head lice quite easily. The tiny white eggs should be combed out of the hair with a fine-toothed comb and the treatment repeated after a week.
You can catch head lice even if your hair is very clean.

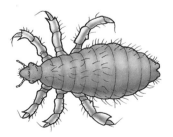

life cycle *noun*
A life cycle is made up of the stages of life from **birth** to **death**. Growing from a **baby** to a **child** and then to an **adolescent** are the three first stages. An adolescent then grows to an **adult**. During adulthood, people reproduce, and more babies are born, starting a new life cycle. In this way, a life cycle is the never-ending circle of birth, death, and birth which keeps the human race alive.
A human body goes through many changes during its life cycle.

life expectancy *noun*
Life expectancy, or lifespan, is the length of time a person may expect to live. A person's life expectancy depends on how long his or her parents lived, and how well his or her health is looked after. People who live in an **environment** with plenty of clean air, water, food, and good medical care usually have a long life expectancy. Females usually have a higher life expectancy than males.
The average life expectancy is shorter in the developing nations than in the developed countries.

lifestyle *noun*
A lifestyle is the way a person lives his or her life. A healthy lifestyle should include regular **exercise**, a balanced **diet**, and rest and relaxation.
He changed to a healthier lifestyle when the doctor told him he had high blood pressure.

ligament *noun*
A ligament is a strong, fibrous band of **tissue**. Ligaments hold the ends of **bones** or **joints** together. They also hold and support other organs inside the body. Ligaments are not elastic, but they are stretchy enough to allow joints to move. A **sprain** happens when a ligament is twisted or torn. Ligaments are often slow to heal.
During the soccer match, she tore a knee ligament and had to limp off the field.

limb *noun*
A limb is an **arm** or a **leg**. Arms are called upper limbs and legs are called lower limbs.
After the crash, her lower limbs were put in plaster so they could heal properly.

lip *noun*
A lip is a fleshy edge or fold of skin around an opening in the body. The **mouth** is surrounded by a pair of lips which open and close. The two pairs of lips that surround the vagina and urethra are called the **labia**.
Lips are sensitive, he discovered when he accidentally bit his.

liver ► page 91

lobe *noun*
1. A lobe is a section of an **organ**. Lobes are usually rounded areas that are separated by bands of tissue. The brain, liver and lungs are all divided into lobes.
The doctor felt the lobe of his liver under the rib cage.
2. The lobe of the ear is the soft, lower part of the outer ear.
A large earring hung from the lobe of her ear.

lockjaw ► **tetanus**

lordosis *noun*
Lordosis is a type of curvature of the **spine**, that forms a hollow area in the small of the back. If someone has lordosis, his or her back curves forward more than it should.
The doctor took an X-ray of her back to see whether she had lordosis.

lumbago *noun*
Lumbago is a kind of **backache** felt in the muscles around the lower parts of the **spine**, especially when lifting something or bending over. Lumbago can be caused by a strain which heals with rest. It may also be a symptom of another illness or back problem.
Many older people have difficulty bending over because of lumbago.

lumbar *adjective*
Lumbar describes anything to do with the lower **back**. The five lumbar vertebrae are in the lower back, between the bottom **rib** and the **pelvis**. A lumbar puncture is a way of drawing out fluid from this part of the **spine** with a needle.
The car seat had a lumbar support, which made it more comfortable to sit in.

lung *noun*
A lung is one of the pair of **organs** used for respiration. The lungs lie on either side of the heart in the **cavity** of the chest, or thorax. Air is breathed in through the mouth and nose, and travels down the **trachea**, **bronchi**, and **bronchioles**. At the end of the bronchioles, the air collects in millions of tiny air sacs called **alveoli**. The lungs are surrounded by two layers of thin membrane called **pleura**.
The doctor put her stethoscope to his chest and listened to his lungs.

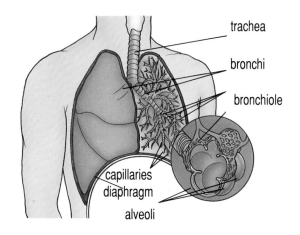

trachea
bronchi
bronchiole
capillaries
diaphragm
alveoli

lymphatic system *noun*
The lymphatic system is a network of small vessels that contain a clear, watery fluid called lymph. Lymphatics vessels collect fluid that has seeped from the **capillaries**, and return it to the **bloodstream**. The lymphatic system is also part of the body's **immune system**. Small lumps called lymph nodes produce some of the **white blood cells** and **antibodies** that fight infection.
Bacteria and waste are filtered from the lymph as it passes through the lymph nodes.

liver *noun*

The liver is the largest **organ** in the body. It is a **gland** which lies on the top right-hand side of the **abdomen**, under the ribs. The liver helps to digest food and keep the blood clean. **Bile** is made in the liver and passed to the **intestine** to help break down food. The liver also takes in and re-uses **nutrients** and other substances from the blood. Poisons in the blood, such as alcohol, are destroyed by the liver.
Most digested food goes to the liver before it goes to the rest of the body.

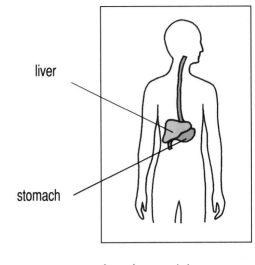

liver

stomach

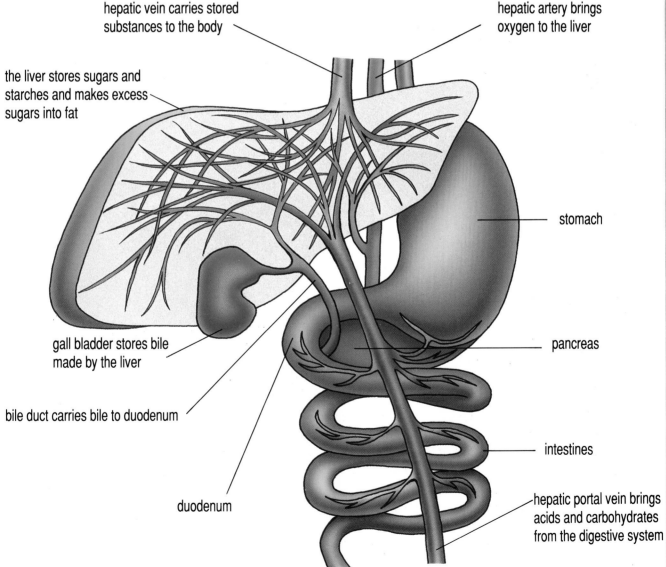

hepatic vein carries stored substances to the body

hepatic artery brings oxygen to the liver

the liver stores sugars and starches and makes excess sugars into fat

stomach

gall bladder stores bile made by the liver

pancreas

bile duct carries bile to duodenum

duodenum

intestines

hepatic portal vein brings acids and carbohydrates from the digestive system

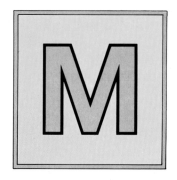

malaria *noun*

Malaria is an infectious **disease** that attacks **red blood cells**. It is caught from the bite of mosquitoes that carry the disease, usually in a tropical country. The first sign of malaria is shivering, followed by several hours of high **fever**, sweating, vomiting, and headache. The symptoms tend to come back frequently until the illness is treated.

He took a course of tablets to avoid catching malaria.

male *adjective*

Male refers to boys and men and behavior usually associated with them. Male is the opposite of **female**.

She gave birth to triplets – one male and two females.

malignant *adjective*

Malignant describes a dangerous illness that may become worse. **Cancer** is a malignant growth, or tumor, in the body. Malignant tumors can sometimes be removed surgically. The opposite of malignant is **benign**.

Someone with a malignant disease needs special medical treatment.

malnutrition *noun*

Malnutrition is ill health caused by not eating enough food, or not eating the right kinds of food. Children with severe malnutrition may develop an illness called **kwashiorkor**, or other illnesses like **scurvy**.

Malnutrition is often found in poorer countries where food is scarce.

mammary gland *noun*

A mammary gland is another term for a **breast**. In women, the two mammary glands grow and develop on the chest during **puberty**. Each fully grown breast contains 15 to 20 milk glands surrounded by fatty tissue. Tubes from the milk glands run toward the tip of the breast, or **nipple**.

After a woman has given birth, the mammary glands start making milk to feed the baby.

mandible ► jawbone

marrow ► bone marrow

massage *noun*

Massage is a way of rubbing and stroking the skin. This can be done by another person's hands, a machine, or flowing water. Massage helps to ease tense and painful muscles underneath the skin. It also improves the circulation of blood and makes a person feel calm and relaxed. Massage is sometimes used to help rebuild muscles after a long illness.

It feels good to relax with a massage after a hard day.

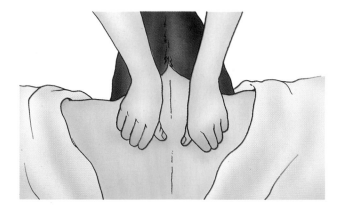

mature *adjective*

Mature means being fully grown. It can describe parts or all of the body. It can also describe personality and behavior. The opposite of mature is **immature**.

The teacher told the boy to behave in a more mature way.

maxilla ► jawbone

measles *noun*
Measles is a common childhood **disease** that is caused by a **virus**. The first symptoms are a fever, sore throat, cough, and runny nose. After four days, blotchy pink spots appear over the face and neck, and spread over the rest of the body. Measles is catching, or contagious, from four days before until five days after the rash appears. There is a vaccine that protects people against measles.
Every child should be vaccinated against measles.

medicine *noun*
Medicine is the study and treatment of disease. It is also a **drug** or any other substance used to treat illness. **Doctors** study and practice medicine and prescribe medicine for patients.
Many kinds of medicine are flavored to make them more pleasant to swallow.

melanin *noun*
Melanin is a dark color, or pigment, found in the skin, hair, and the iris of the eye. Melanin protects the body from the sun by tanning, or turning the skin a darker color.
As the girl sunbathed, melanin turned her skin a shade darker.

melanoma *noun*
Melanoma is a cancer of the **skin**. A harmful growth, or **malignant tumor**, forms in a pigment cell of the skin or eyes. The growth may spread to the lymph glands and to the rest of the body and can be fatal. **Moles** and **freckles** that changes color or shape, itch or bleed need to be seen by a doctor because they could be cancerous.
People who spend long in the sun may develop melanoma.

membrane *noun*
A membrane is a skin inside the body. Membranes are made of thin layers of tissue that cover and separate **organs**. They also line the inside of tubes and **cavities** inside the body.
Fluid is filtered through a membrane in the kidney.

memory *noun*
Memory is a store of information in the **brain**. It is also the ability to remember the information in the right order. Some information is stored in the memory for a short time, while other things remain there for a long time. The part of the brain that controls memory is called the **cerebral cortex**. Memory is part of the thinking ability, or **intellect**, of the mind.
She recited the poem from memory.

meningitis *noun*
Meningitis is an **inflammation** of the **membranes** that cover the brain and spinal cord, caused by **bacteria** or a **virus**. The first signs may be a sore throat and slight symptoms of flu, followed by a severe headache, fever, and a stiff neck. The eyes may also be very sensitive to light. Vomiting, convulsions, and coma may follow. Some kinds of meningitis are difficult to treat.
The child was rushed to the hospital because meningitis was suspected.

menstrual cycle *noun*
The menstrual cycle is the process in which a woman's body is prepared for pregnancy. Beginning at **puberty**, every month an egg from one of the two **ovaries** travels along a **Fallopian tube** toward the **uterus**. This is called **ovulation**. If the egg is fertilized, it will settle into the lining of the uterus to grow into a baby. If the egg is not fertilized, the egg and lining are passed out through the **vagina** with blood. Then the process begins again. The menstrual cycle usually ends when a woman is around 45-50 years old.
The menstrual cycle lasts about 28 days.

menstruation   *noun*
Menstruation is a part of the **menstrual cycle** of a female. It is the period of bleeding from the **vagina** when the lining of the uterus is shed. This usually lasts from three to seven days. The flow of blood is normally heaviest in the first two days.
She started her menstruation at the age of thirteen.

mental illness   *noun*
Mental illness refers to disorders of the **mind**. Doctors who treat people with mental illnesses are called **psychiatrists**. There are many causes for mental illness. Some types run in families and are passed through **genes**, while others are due to problems in a person's life. Damage to the brain can also cause mental illness. Some mental illnesses last only a short time and can be completely cured.
Mental illness affects behavior and the way a person thinks.

metabolic rate   *noun*
Metabolic rate is the speed at which a body burns **energy**. Every part of the body is using energy all the time, even when a person is asleep. People get their energy from food and from fat stored in the body. A person's metabolic rate is controlled by **hormones** produced in the **thyroid gland**.
Some people burn energy faster than others; they have a higher metabolic rate.

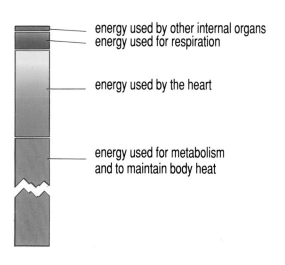

energy used by other internal organs
energy used for respiration

energy used by the heart

energy used for metabolism
and to maintain body heat

metabolism   *noun*
Metabolism is all the work carried out by the body in order to grow, heal itself, and replace tissue. Chemicals and other substances are produced by the body. At the same time, the body is breaking down food, to provide energy to do all these things. This whole process is called metabolism.
Some people's metabolism works slowly and can result in their being overweight.

metacarpals ► hand

metatarsals ► foot

microbiology   *noun*
Microbiology is the study of tiny living things that can be seen only under a microscope. These include **bacteria** and **viruses**. Medical microbiologists study diseases caused by bacteria and viruses, and research ways to prevent and cure these diseases.
Dental microbiologists study the germs that are found in the mouth and on the teeth.

microsurgery   *noun*
Microsurgery is a kind of surgical operation in which microscopes are used to help a surgeon operate on delicate parts of the body, such as nerve endings, or the brain, ear, or eye. The surgeon uses specially adapted instruments in microsurgery. Sometimes an image of the part of the body that is being operated on is displayed on a television screen during surgery.
The doctor used microsurgery to repair the boy's severed finger.

middle ear   *noun*
The middle ear is part of the **ear**. The **eardrum** separates the middle ear from the outer ear. The middle ear is filled with air from the back of the nose by the **Eustachian tube**. Sound waves pass through the eardrum to three tiny bones in the middle ear called the **ossicles**. The ossicles vibrate with the sound waves.
Fluid in the middle ear can cause deafness.

midwife *noun*
A midwife is a person trained to help pregnant women before, during, and after **childbirth**. Most midwives are specially trained nurses who check on the health of the mother and unborn baby during pregnancy. Then, after delivering the baby, the midwife helps teach the new mother how to care for the child.
The midwife helped the woman give birth.

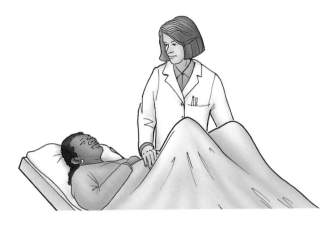

migraine *noun*
A migraine is a type of **headache** with a severe, throbbing **pain** that lasts for hours or days. It is often in only one side of the head. A person with migraine may feel nauseous, the light may hurt his or her eyes. Migraines may be caused by a reaction to certain foods, such as chocolates or cheese, bright lights, loud noises, or stress.
A person with a migraine should lie down in a dark room.

milk *noun*
Milk is a liquid food made by the **mammary glands** of a female mammal after the birth of a baby. Milk is a complete food, which means that it has most of the **nutrients** people need to live. Human milk is the best food for babies for the first few months. Cow's milk is an important part of most people's diets after the age of one year and is a good source of calcium.
Breastfed babies grow strong on their mother's milk.

mind *noun*
Mind is another word for the intellect. It is the part of a person that thinks, has feelings, and understands. Mind is the part of a person that is not the body. All the parts of the mind make up a person's personality. The body and the mind together make up a whole person.
The imagination is part of the mind.

mineral *noun*
A mineral is one of many substances found in soil, water, rock, and metal. Some minerals are necessary to keep the body healthy. **Calcium** is important for teeth and bones, and **iron** is needed for healthy blood. A balanced **diet** provides all the minerals a person's body needs. It is not usually necessary to take extra minerals in tablet form.
You need to eat foods containing the mineral calcium to develop strong bones.

miscarriage *noun*
A miscarriage is the loss of a **fetus** in the early part of **pregnancy**. Most miscarriages occur because there is something wrong with the fetus. The first signs of a miscarriage are pains in the **abdomen** and bleeding from the **vagina**.
Women who have miscarriages can later give birth to healthy babies.
miscarry *verb*

molar ► tooth

mole *noun*
A mole is a dark spot on the **skin**. Moles vary in size, shape, and color. They can be flat and smooth or raised and hairy. Moles are caused by a dark pigment in the skin called **melanin**. Most moles are harmless, but some can cause health problems. A mole that changes shape or color should be seen by a doctor.
The doctor removed the large mole growing on the patient's chin.

movement *noun*

Movement is the act of changing from one position to another. The body is able to make many different kinds of movements through a network of **muscles**, **tendons**, and **ligaments**. Every movement a person makes is a result of messages from the **nerves** to the muscles. Movements are controlled by the **brain**, and the **ears** and **eyes** are also often involved.

With a jerky movement, he swept the cup off the table.

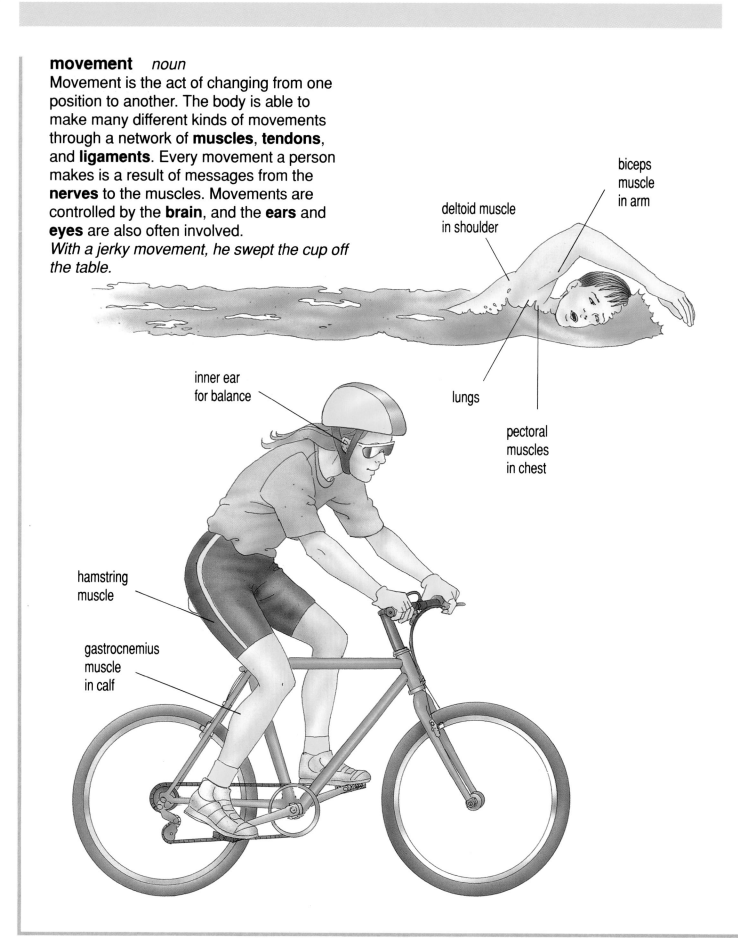

biceps muscle in arm

deltoid muscle in shoulder

lungs

pectoral muscles in chest

inner ear for balance

hamstring muscle

gastrocnemius muscle in calf

inner ear for sound and balance

thigh muscles

pelvis

gastrocnemius muscles in calves

eyes coordinate movements of hand

small muscles in hand

inner ear for sound

muscles in forearm

eyes coordinate movements of hands

finger muscles

muscle   *noun*
Muscle is strong, stretchy **tissue**. There are over 600 muscles arranged around the frame of the **skeleton** and inside the body. Muscles are able to contract, or tighten, into a shorter, fatter shape. By doing this they make parts of the body move. The muscles attached to bones usually work in pairs, such as the **biceps** and **triceps**.
Muscle makes up nearly half the body weight of an adult.

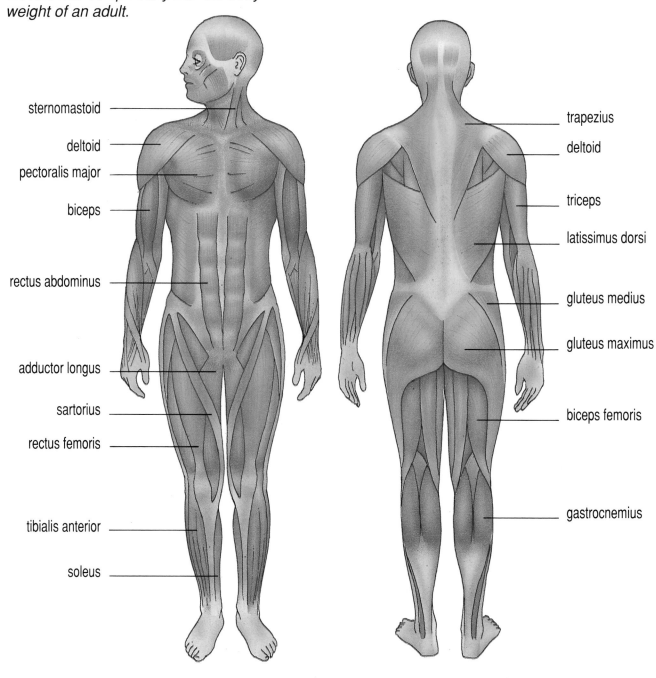

sternomastoid

deltoid

pectoralis major

biceps

rectus abdominus

adductor longus

sartorius

rectus femoris

tibialis anterior

soleus

trapezius

deltoid

triceps

latissimus dorsi

gluteus medius

gluteus maximus

biceps femoris

gastrocnemius

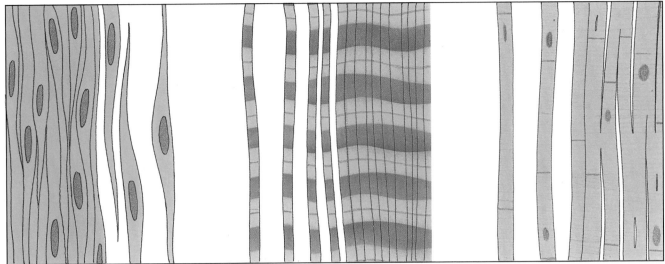

Involuntary or smooth muscle in the stomach and intestines. These muscles work automatically. They cannot be controlled.

Voluntary, or striated (striped) muscles, for moving the skeleton. These muscles can be controlled at will.

Cardiac muscles in the heart. These muscles work automatically. They cannot be controlled.

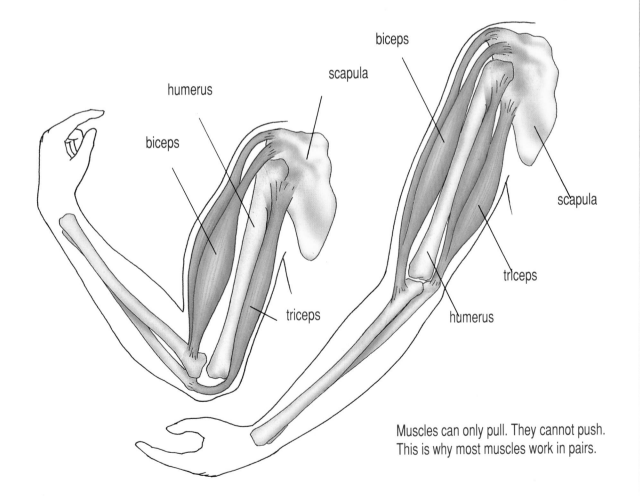

biceps

scapula

humerus

biceps

triceps

biceps

scapula

triceps

humerus

Muscles can only pull. They cannot push. This is why most muscles work in pairs.

molecule *noun*
A molecule is a small particle. Molecules are the smallest complete part of any substance, and contain two or more atoms that are joined together.
The molecules in a liquid or a gas move about easily.

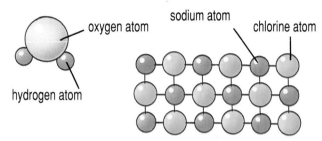

water molecule   salt molecule

mononucleosis *noun*
Mononucleosis is an **infectious disease** caused by a **virus**. It is most often caught by young people between 15 and 25 years. The first **symptoms** are tiredness, and a slight **fever**. This lasts for a week to 10 days. A sore throat and high fever then develop. The glands in the neck swell and there may be a faint, pink **rash** over the body. This part of the illness lasts for another week to 10 days.
Mononucleosis is often called the 'kissing disease'.

motor *adjective*
Motor describes something to do with movement in the body. Motor nerves send signals to muscles to make them move. The motor cortex is part of the brain.
The disabled boy needed to improve the motor control in his legs.

mouth *noun*
A mouth is the opening in the **face** formed by the upper and lower **jawbones**. **Lips** surround the entrance of the mouth. Inside are the **gums**, **teeth**, **palate**, and **tongue**. The soft skin inside the mouth is kept moist with **saliva** and **mucus**. Mouths are used for eating and speaking and sometimes also for breathing.
The mouth is the beginning of the alimentary canal.

movement ► page 96

mucous membrane *noun*
A mucous membrane is a moist layer of **skin**. The surface is kept moist by tiny glands that release a sticky fluid called **mucus**. Mucous membranes line many parts of the inside of the body. They also line the inside of the openings of the body, such as the **mouth** and the **vagina**.
The hot food burned the mucous membranes in her mouth.

mucus *noun*
Mucus is a sticky fluid made by a **mucous membrane**. Mucus protects and cleans the surface of a membrane. It also makes it slippery and smooth. Some mucus contains **enzymes** that help to break down substances, such as **food**.
She coughed up mucus when she had bronchitis.

multiple sclerosis *noun*
Multiple sclerosis is a **disease** that attacks the **nerves** in the **brain** and **spinal cord**. The development of the disease can be very slow. Symptoms start with tingling and numb feelings in the skin. A person may then lose control of his or her **muscles**. People recover between attacks, but each time the illness returns, the symptoms are worse and stay longer.
There is no cure for multiple sclerosis.

mumps *noun*
Mumps is a common childhood **disease** caused by a **virus**. It can be a more serious illness when caught by an adult. The first sign of mumps may be a **headache**, **fever**, and vomiting. A day or two later, the **glands** around one or both ears become swollen and painful. It may be painful to open the mouth and swallow. The swelling can last for five or six days. Mumps remains **infectious** from about three days after the swelling goes down.
There is a vaccine to protect people against catching mumps.

muscle ▶ page 98

muscular *adjective*
Muscular describes anything to do with **muscles**. Regular **exercise** develops strong, muscular bodies.
The champion weight lifter had very muscular thighs.

muscular dystrophy *noun*
Muscular dystrophy is a group of **diseases** in which the **muscles** attached to the **bones** waste away and do not work properly. The disease gradually gets worse over a number of years. Muscular dystrophy is **hereditary**, or passed on in families through faulty **genes**. More boys than girls are born with the disease. There is no cure for muscular dystrophy.
People with muscular dystrophy feel weak and find it difficult to move.

myopia *noun*
Myopia is being able to see objects clearly when they are near, but not at a distance. The nonmedical name for myopia is near-sightedness. People suffer from myopia if the lens of the eye is too curved, or the eyeball too long. Light is then focused in front of the **retina** at the back of the eye instead of on it. **Far-sightedness** is the opposite of myopia.
Wearing eyeglasses or contact lenses corrects myopia.
myopic *adjective*

nail *noun*
A nail is a piece of hard **tissue** made of **keratin**. Nails grow at the end of each **finger** and **toe**. The whitish, semi-circular area near the base is called the lunula. Toenails are tougher than fingernails and grow more slowly. A change in the color or shape of nails can be a sign of an illness.
Nails protect the ends of people's fingers and toes.

narcotic *noun*
A narcotic is a strong **drug** that relieves pain and makes a person feel drowsy. Narcotic drugs can be dangerous when taken without a **doctor's** supervision.
A narcotic drug can become addictive.
narcotic *adjective*

nasal *adjective*
Nasal describes anything to do with the **nose**. Air passes through the nasal passages in the nostrils when a person breathes.
The nasal bone lies under the nose, on the face.

nausea *noun*
Nausea is the feeling of wanting to **vomit**. Bringing up the contents of the stomach often gives relief. Nausea may be a symptom of stomach upsets, food poisoning, **pregnancy**, travel sickness, or shock. It can also be a **symptom** of other kinds of illness.
The man suffered from nausea when the sea was rough.
nauseous *adjective*

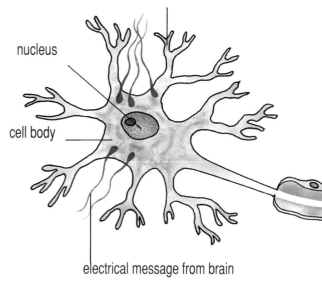

dendrites receive messages

nucleus

cell body

electrical message from brain

nervous system *noun*

The nervous system is a network of **nerve cells** called neurons, that send information to and from all parts of the body. The **brain** and **spinal cord** are called the central nervous system. Messages, or nervous impulses, travel along nerves that connect the brain to the rest of the body. All the activities of the body, such as breathing and moving, are controlled by the nervous system.

Motor neuron disease affects the nervous system.

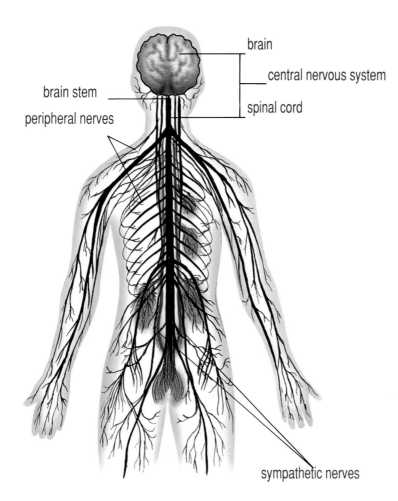

brain

central nervous system

spinal cord

brain stem

peripheral nerves

sympathetic nerves

The central nervous system consists of the brain and the spinal cord.

The peripheral nervous system involves nerves that are linked with the central nervous system and branch through the body.

The autonomic nervous system is responsible for controlling the automatic activity of internal organs. Part of this system is called the sympathetic system. Sympathetic nerves form two cords that run parallel to the spinal cord. They are responsible for actions such as speeding up the heartbeat.

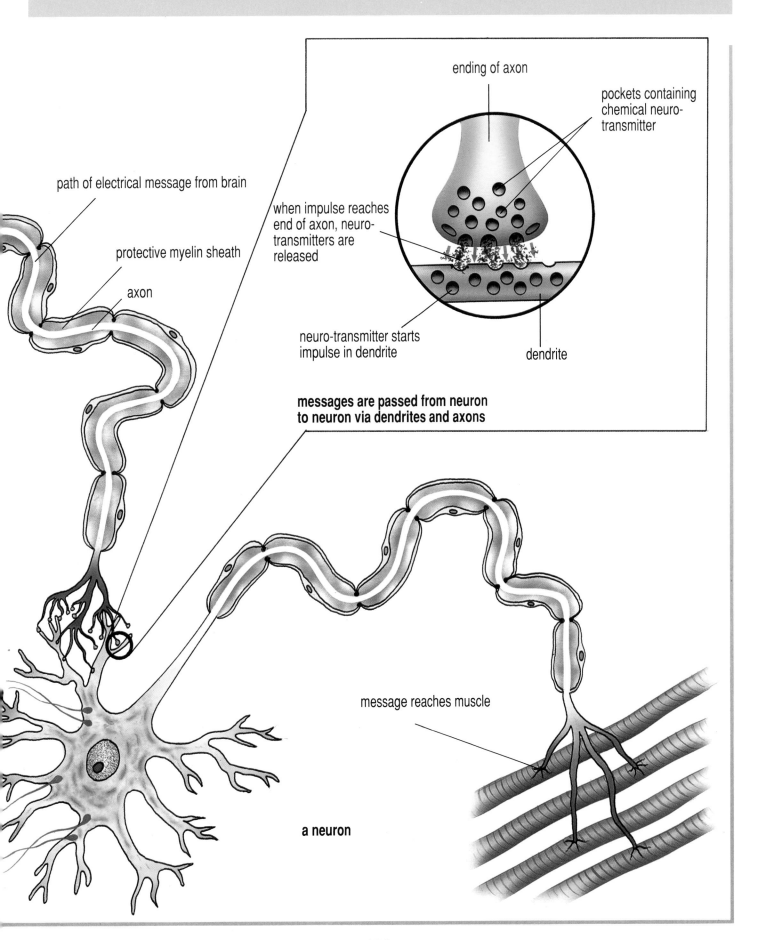

path of electrical message from brain

protective myelin sheath

axon

ending of axon

pockets containing chemical neuro-transmitter

when impulse reaches end of axon, neuro-transmitters are released

neuro-transmitter starts impulse in dendrite

dendrite

messages are passed from neuron to neuron via dendrites and axons

message reaches muscle

a neuron

navel *noun*
The navel is the healed end of the **umbilical cord** in the middle of the outside of the **abdomen**. Navels may be a small hollow in the skin or a small, knotted lump that sticks out. The navel is the point where a person was joined to his or her mother in the uterus by the umbilical cord. This cord is cut soon after birth. The stump that is left shrivels away, falls off and leaves a navel.
The navel is also called the bellybutton.

near-sightedness ► myopia

neck *noun*
The neck is the narrow part of the body between the **head** and the **shoulders**. The seven bones of the neck, or the **cervical vertebrae**, support the head and allow it to move. **Blood vessels** run through the neck and connect the **brain** and other parts of the head with the rest of the body. The organs in the neck include the **trachea**, **esophagus**, and **thyroid gland**.
She had a whiplash injury which caused a stiff neck.

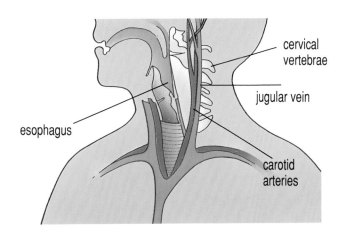

cervical vertebrae

jugular vein

esophagus

carotid arteries

nephron *noun*
A nephron is a tiny tube in a **kidney**. Over a million nephrons in each kidney filter water, salts, and glucose from the **blood**. The waste liquid left behind is then passed from the kidney and out of the body as **urine**.
A kidney dialysis machine does the job of the nephrons.

nerve *noun*
A nerve is a bundle of **fibers** in the **nervous system**. Messages pass through nerves on their way to and from the **brain**. The brain uses nerves to pass on instructions to every part of the body. The main nerves work in pairs and start from the **brain stem** and the **spinal cord**. They branch out through the body in long strands covered by a sheath of **connective tissue**.
The pinched nerve at the base of his spine caused him great pain.

nerve ending *noun*
A nerve ending is the end of one of the **fibers** of a **nerve**. Nerve endings touch other nerves, **glands**, **muscles**, and other **tissues** in the body. **Motor nerve** endings instruct muscles to move. **Sensory nerve** endings in the **skin** pick up messages of pain, heat, and cold.
The exposed nerve ending caused a bad toothache.

nervous system ► page 102

neuron *noun*
A neuron is one of the main units that make up the **nerves**. It consists of a **cell** body with threadlike parts that carry signals to and from the cells. Billions of different kinds of neurons make up the **nervous system** in the body.
The message was sent from the brain to the muscle through a string of neurons.

nipple *noun*
A nipple is the small, brownish or pink teat in the center of each **breast**. Nipples are surrounded by a ring of the same colored skin called the areola. During puberty, a girl's nipples and areolae become larger and darker. An infant sucks milk out of tiny openings in the nipples during **breastfeeding**.
The newborn baby fed from its mother's nipple.

nose ► page 105

nose   *noun*

The nose is the central feature of a face. Two small bones meet in the center to form the bridge of the nose. The tip of the nose and nostrils are shaped with **cartilage** and skin. The inside of the nose is lined with a **mucous membrane** and joins the airways at the back of the thoat. Air is warmed, cleaned, and moistened as it travels through the nose on its way to the **lungs**. Smells are picked up by nerve endings at the top of the inside of the nose.

Noses are for breathing and smelling.

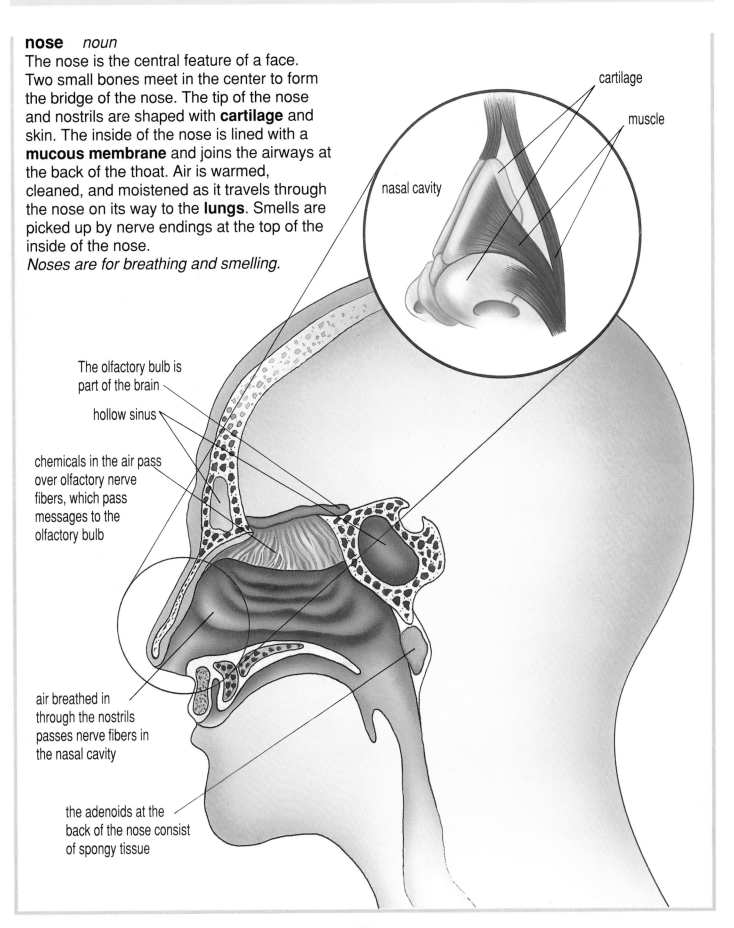

cartilage

muscle

nasal cavity

The olfactory bulb is part of the brain

hollow sinus

chemicals in the air pass over olfactory nerve fibers, which pass messages to the olfactory bulb

air breathed in through the nostrils passes nerve fibers in the nasal cavity

the adenoids at the back of the nose consist of spongy tissue

nosebleed　*noun*

A nosebleed is bleeding from one or both **nostrils**. Sneezing, blowing, or picking the nose can all make it bleed. Pinching the nose should stop the flow of blood. Nosebleeds may also be a **symptom** of a blood disorder or other illness.

People sometimes get nosebleeds at high altitudes.

nostril　*noun*

A nostril is one of the two openings in the **nose**. Nostrils are divided by a piece of thin **bone** and **cartilage**. The two channels of the nostrils lead toward the nasal cavity, which is the space that lies between the floor of the **skull** and the roof of the **mouth**.

When he had a cold, his nostrils were clogged with mucus.

nucleus　*noun*

A nucleus is the center of a **cell**. The nucleus of each cell contains **chromosomes**, **genes**, and the **DNA** that forms them.

The nucleus is the control center of each cell.

nurse　*noun*

A nurse is a person trained to treat people who are ill. Some nurses have special training to look after certain kinds of illness or patients. Nurses also help with operations and check-ups. For example, geriatric nurses look after old people.

She wanted to go to school to learn to be a nurse.

nutrient　*noun*

A nutrient is a substance in food. The body needs nutrients for **energy**, **growth**, and good **health**. The important nutrients in food are **proteins**, **carbohydrates**, **fats**, **vitamins**, and **minerals**.

The nutrients in processed food are listed on the outside of the package.

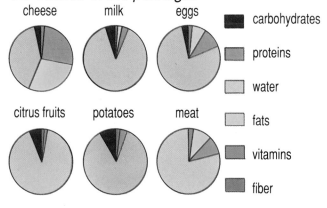

nutrition　*noun*

Nutrition is the study of **food** and **health**. It is also the whole process of how people prepare, eat, and **digest** food to keep the body in good working order. People need to eat a balanced **diet** to stay healthy. This must contain the right amounts of **nutrients**, **fiber**, and fluids.

Good nutrition is essential for good health.

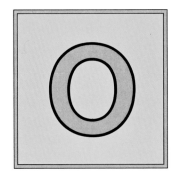

olfactory   *adjective*
Olfactory describes anything to do with the **nose** and the sense of smell.
His olfactory senses detected the food.

operation   *noun*
An operation is a medical treatment that repairs, replaces, or removes **organs** inside the body. People are given **drugs** called **anesthetics** to deaden pain or make them **unconscious**. Then a surgeon cuts open the skin and after the operation, sews it up again to help it to **heal**.
After the operation on her eye, she could see clearly again.

optic   *adjective*
Optic describes anything to do with the **eye** or **sight.**
Visual messages are transmitted to the brain by the optic nerves.

optician   *noun*
An optician is a person who helps to correct **eye** problems. Opticians make and fit lenses for eyeglasses and **contact lenses**.
The optician checked her lenses.

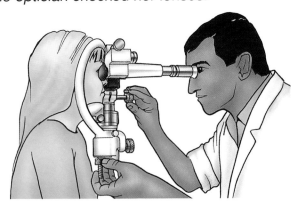

oral   *adjective*
Oral describes anything to do with the **mouth**. Medicine taken orally is put into the mouth and swallowed.
Brushing the teeth is an important part of oral hygiene.

orbit   *noun*
An orbit is one of two bony sockets in the face. The **eyeballs** fit into the orbits in a bed of fatty **tissue**. Six **muscles** attach the eyeball to the orbit and allow it to move. The eyes are linked to the **brain** through a hole at the back of each orbit.
The orbits help to protect the eyes from injury.

organ   *noun*
An organ is any part of a body that carries out a particular job, such as the **liver** or the **heart**. The **ears** are organs of hearing and balance. Organs may be made of any kind of two or more **tissues** and may be any size or shape.
The heart and the brain are two of the most important organs in the human body.

organic   *adjective*
1. Organic describes anything to do with an organ.
Pneumonia is an organic disease of the lung.
2. Organic also refers to natural substances formed in or from plants or animals.
Organic gardeners do not use chemical fertilizers.

ossicles   *plural noun*
Ossicles are three tiny bones in the **middle ear** that vibrate when sound waves pass through the **eardrum**. Two small muscles attach the ossicles to the bone around them. When a loud sound passes through the middle ear, the muscles tighten. This stops the ossicles from vibrating too much and damaging the inner ear.
The ossicles are called the hammer, the anvil, and the stirrup.

ossification *noun*

Ossification is the forming of **bone**. This happens as a baby develops in the **uterus** before it is born, and ossification continues as children grow into adults. During **adolescence**, bones reach their full size. A person grows taller and broader in this last stage of ossification.

The bone in a broken leg knits together by ossification.

osteopathy *noun*

Osteopathy is a way of treating **illness** and relieving pain. It is an alternative **medicine** carried out by trained people called osteopaths. Bones, joints, muscles, ligaments, and tendons are moved and massaged by hand with this type of treatment. Osteopathy deals with all kinds of disorders of the skeleton and nervous systems.

The football player's leg was treated by osteopathy.

otitis media *noun*

Otitis media is an infection of the **middle ear**. This part of the ear becomes inflamed and full of pus, causing very painful earache, a fever and temporary deafness. When someone has a cold, the infection can get into the middle ear through the **Eustachian tube** at the back of the nose. If the pus builds up it may burst the eardrum, which relieves the pain. Antibiotic drugs and draining out the pus are treatments for otitis media.

Otitis media is often caused by virus infections.

outer ear *noun*

The outer ear is the shell of skin and cartilage that has a funnel-shaped canal leading to the **middle ear**. The outer ear is separated from the middle ear by the **eardrum**, through which sound waves pass. Fine hairs and wax inside the outer ear protect the ear from dust and other particles.

The outer ear is where the process of hearing begins.

ovary *noun*

An ovary is a female sex organ inside the **pelvis**. The two ovaries are about the size of walnuts and are located on either side of the **uterus**. The arms of the **Fallopian tubes** curve over and meet the ovaries. Ovaries make and store **ova** and produce **hormones** that help to control the **menstrual cycle**.

Hormones cause the ovaries to release eggs during ovulation.

ovarian adjective

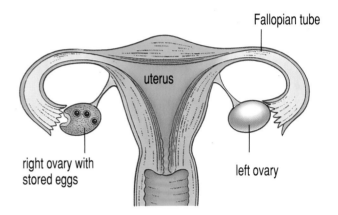

Fallopian tube

uterus

right ovary with stored eggs

left ovary

ovulation *noun*

Ovulation is the release of an **ovum** from an **ovary**. One mature ovum is released half-way through the **menstrual cycle** every month. The egg travels along the **Fallopian tube** from the ovary to the **uterus**. If it is not fertilized, the ovum leaves the body during **menstruation.**

Ovulation is the time when a woman is at her most fertile.

ovum (plural ova) *noun*

An ovum is a female egg that consists of one cell. An ovum has 23 **chromosomes**, half the usual number. A male **sperm** is the only other kind of cell with 23 chromosomes. An ovum is released every month from an **ovary** and travels through a **Fallopian tube** to the **uterus**. When a sperm meets and **fertilizes** an ovum, the chromosomes pair up to make an **embryo**.

An unfertilized ovum passes out of the body during menstruation.

oxygen *noun*
Oxygen is a gas in the air. It has no smell or color and makes up one fifth of normal air. Humans need oxygen to live. It is absorbed into the **blood** from the air breathed into the **lungs**.
Plants produce oxygen during photosynthesis.

pacemaker *noun*
A pacemaker is part of a **heart**. It is a small area of **tissue** that controls the **heartbeat**. It does this by sending out an electric signal that tells the heart how fast and how often to pump out **blood**. If the heart's own pacemaker fails, an **artificial** one can be fitted under the skin in the chest. Wires from the pacemaker are connected to the heart.
The electronic pacemaker prolonged his life.

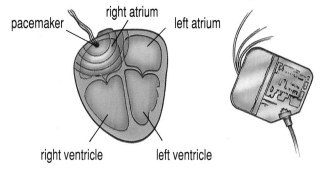

pacemaker · right atrium · left atrium · right ventricle · left ventricle

pain *noun*
Pain is a hurt somewhere in the body, when **sensory nerves** carry pain signals to the **brain**. Pain disappears as an injury heals or the illness is treated. Severe pain can be eased with **drugs** called **analgesics**.
Most pain is a sign of injury or illness.

palate *noun*
The palate is the roof of the **mouth**. The hard palate in front is made of bone. The soft palate curves down toward the back of the throat. This part of the palate is made of muscle and ends in a small lump of tissue called the **uvula**.
The palate helps you to swallow food without choking.

109

palm *noun*
A palm is the inside part of a **hand**. Palms start from the wrist and end at the base of the fingers.
Lines criss-cross the palm of your hand.

pancreas *noun*
The pancreas is a **gland** in the **abdomen**. It is about 6 inches long and lies behind the **stomach** where it is joined to the **small intestine**. Juices from the pancreas help to break down, or **digest**, food. The pancreas also makes **insulin**, a **hormone** that controls the level of sugar in the **blood**.
He suffered from diabetes because his pancreas made too little insulin.

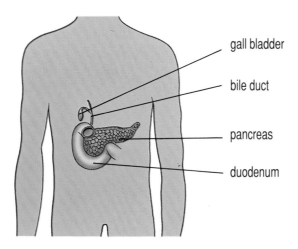

gall bladder

bile duct

pancreas

duodenum

pandemic *adjective*
Pandemic describes any **disease** that affects many people in a large area of the world. A disease that spreads across a smaller area is described as **epidemic**.
Malaria is a pandemic disease, found in most tropical countries.

paralysis *noun*
Paralysis means not being able to move. This may be in part or all of the body. Paralysis may affect a person for only a short time or for the rest of his or her life. Most paralysis is caused by damage to the **nerves** that tell the **muscles** to move. This can happen through a disease or an injury.
Total paralysis from the neck down is called quadriplegia.

parasite ▶ worm

parathyroid gland *noun*
The parathyroid gland is one of four small organs in the neck. There are two on each side of the **thyroid gland**. Parathyroid glands release a **hormone** that controls the level of calcium in the **blood**.
Parathyroid glands are part of the endocrine system.

parent *noun*
A parent is the mother or father of a child.
Parents provide love, care, and training for their children.

patella ▶ kneecap

pathogen *noun*
A pathogen is any substance that causes a disease. Some types of **bacteria** are pathogens because they enter the body and cause infections.
Pathogens in the drinking water caused him to become ill.

patient *noun*
A patient is a person who is receiving care or treatment from a doctor.
The patients lay on their beds in the hospital ward.

pectoral *adjective*
Pectoral describes anything to do with the **chest**.
He did a lot of heavy weightlifting to develop his pectoral muscles.

pelvis *noun*
The pelvis is the part of the **skeleton** where the legs join the rest of the body. It is a hollow cradle of bone that protects the organs in the lower **abdomen**. The hipbones and lower backbone fuse together to form the pelvis. The main bones of the pelvis are called the **hipbone**, **sacrum**, and **coccyx**.
The old man fell and broke his pelvis.
pelvic *adjective*

penicillin *noun*
Penicillin is one of a group of **drugs** called **antibiotics**, which fight harmful **bacteria** in the human body. Penicillin was first made from mold, after it was noticed that certain types of mold could kill some of the bacteria that cause **infections**. Some forms of penicillin are now made synthetically. A few people are allergic to penicillin.
A British scientist named Alexander Fleming discovered penicillin in 1928.

penis *noun*
The penis is the **male** sex **organ**. The penis lies over the **scrotum**, between the legs. In uncircumcized men and boys, the head of the penis is covered by the **foreskin. Urine** and **semen** pass out of the penis through a tube called the **urethra.**
In circumcision, the foreskin of the penis is removed.

people in medicine ► page 112

pepsin *noun*
Pepsin is an **enzyme** that helps to **digest** food. It is found in the juices made by the walls of the **stomach**. Pepsin breaks down the **proteins** in food into smaller particles.
Pepsin is just one of the enzymes that help us to digest the food we eat.

peristalsis *noun*
Peristalsis is a series of muscle movements in the esophagus, stomach and intestines.
Peristalsis pushes food along the intestines.

peritoneum *noun*
The peritoneum is a thin **membrane** inside the body. It lines the inside of the **abdomen** and wraps and protects all the organs in the abdomen, such as the **stomach**, the **kidneys**, and the **liver**. The thickest part of the peritoneum supports the **intestines** at the back of the abdomen. It also links the intestines with the **lymphatic system**.
A puncture of the peritoneum can be extremely painful.

peritonitis *noun*
Peritonitis is an infection of the **peritoneum**. This infection causes part of the peritoneum to become inflamed. A person will feel severe pain in the **abdomen** and may have a **fever**. Peritonitis is usually caused by an infection of one of the **organs** inside the abdomen, such as the **appendix**.
The child developed peritonitis and had to be rushed to the hospital.

phalanges *plural noun*
The phalanges are the **bones** of the **fingers** and **toes**. There are two bones in each of the thumbs and big toes. The rest of the fingers and toes have three bones each. A single bone of the toe or finger is called a phalanx.
He broke one of the phalanges in his finger when he shut it in the train door.

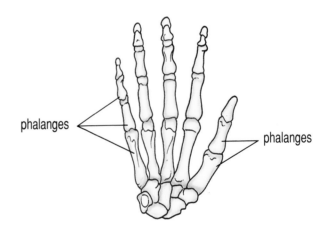

pharmacy *noun*
1. A pharmacy is a place where **medicines** are made and supplied. Most **hospitals** have their own pharmacy. Pharmacists are people trained to prepare medicines.
From his pharmacy, the pharmacist filled many prescriptions.
2. Pharmacy is the process of making medicines to treat illness. Scientists use all kinds of natural or synthetic substances to make **drugs** and other medicines.
She went to school for a degree in pharmacy.
pharmaceutical *adjective*

people in medicine   *noun*
People in medicine have always searched
for ways to treat **illnesses** and **injuries**.
Thousands of years ago in India, surgical
operations were performed using
instruments much like those in use today.
The Ancient Chinese developed
acupuncture, and used plants as medicines.
Over the years, scientists have made
discoveries that help them to understand
how to prevent illness and give the best
treatment.
Modern technology helps people in medicine
to treat many kinds of disease and injury.

Edward Jenner 1749–1823
Jenner was a British doctor who discovered vaccination.
He found that if someone was injected with a mild form of
cowpox germs, he or she became immune to smallpox.

Andreas Vesalius 1514–1564
Vesalius was a Flemish doctor who made the first accurate
anatomical studies of the human body. He did much of his
research at his medical school in Italy.

Louis Pasteur 1822–1895
The French scientist Pasteur discovered that bacteria can
cause disease. He found that heat killed the bacteria.
He also discovered ways of weakening harmful germs so
that they could be used as vaccines.

Wilhelm Roentgen 1845–1923
Roentgen was a German physicist who discovered X-rays in 1895. His work encouraged other physicists to study other types of invisible radiation.

Shibasaburo Kitasato 1852–1931
The Japanese scientist Kitasato studied the bacteria that cause tetanus and diphtheria, and also discovered the bacterium that causes bubonic plague. Kitasato founded a laboratory near Tokyo, Japan, where infectious diseases were studied.

Pierre Curie 1859–1906
Marie Curie 1867–1934
The Curies were French scientists who discovered the radioactive substance called radium. After her husband's death, Marie Curie devoted much of her time to the medical use of radioactive substances.

Alexander Fleming 1881–1955
Fleming was a Scottish scientist who discovered penicillin, a mold that can kill germs. This discovery led to the development of antibiotics, which greatly reduce the risk of infection after an injury or surgery.

pharynx *noun*
A pharynx is part of a **throat**. The tube of the pharynx joins the back of the **nose** and **mouth** to the **larynx**. It is a moist and muscular pathway for air and food. The sounds made by the larynx use the space of the pharynx as an echo chamber. The pharynx also contains the **tonsils** and the **adenoids.**
He had a sore throat due to an infection of his pharynx.

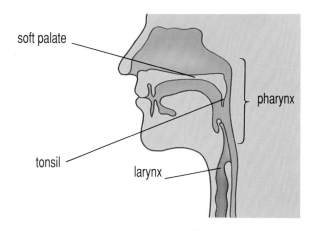

phlegm noun
Phlegm is the thick **mucus** that sometimes collects in the nose and throat. People have phlegm when they have a cold.
Her throat was so blocked with phlegm that she could hardly breathe.

phobia *noun*
A phobia is a strong fear of something. This may be of an animal, such as a spider, or it may be a fear of other things, such as heights, or the dark. Agoraphobia is a fear of being outside. Claustrophobia is a fear of being shut in.
Since he was a child, he had had a phobia of mice.

physiology *noun*
Physiology is a science that studies living **cells**, **tissues**, and **organs** to see how they work. A person who studies this subject is called a physiologist.
The class studied physiology to learn about the human body.

pigment *noun*
A pigment is a substance that gives color. The pigment in **blood** is red, and a pigment in **bile** gives it a yellowish-green color. The pigment in skin is called **melanin**.
Freckles are caused by particles of pigment in the skin.

piles ► **hemorrhoids**

pimple ► **skin blemish**

pituitary gland *noun*
The pituitary gland is a small **organ** at the base of the **brain**. It is joined to the **hypothalamus**, which is the part of the brain that controls eating, drinking, and body heat. The pituitary gland is the main part of the **endocrine system** and instructs all the other glands to work by releasing **hormones**. In a female the pituitary gland also releases hormones that start **childbirth** and **breast-feeding**.
The pituitary gland releases a growth hormone that determines how tall we grow.

pivot joint ► **joint**

placenta *noun*
A placenta is an **organ** in a pregnant female through which the **fetus** is fed. The **umbilical cord** links the fetus to the placenta, which also takes away waste substances. The placenta is passed out of the **vagina** after **childbirth**.
Food and oxygen pass from the mother to the baby through the placenta.
placental *adjective*

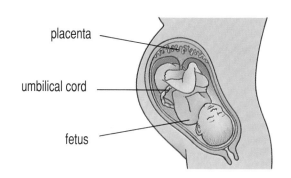

plaque *noun*
Plaque is a substance that builds into a covering. **Bacteria**, saliva, and food particles form a hard, scaly layer on teeth known as plaque. This type of plaque can cause gum disease and tooth decay, or **caries**. A scabby patch of **skin** is also known as plaque. The third kind of plaque in the body is the layer of **fat** that sometimes lines the blood vessels.
His teeth were decaying because he never brushed the plaque off them.

plasma *noun*
Plasma is the pale yellow fluid that surrounds the tiny **blood cells** and **platelets** that make up **blood**. Plasma is a solution of water, salts, and chemicals. This fluid carries substances, such as **sugar** and **hormones**, to all parts of the body. Plasma also removes waste products. It is possible to give plasma by **transfusion**.
Plasma is the fluid that makes up most of your blood.

plaster cast *noun*
A plaster cast is a mixture of powder and water that sets hard. It is used to support broken **bones** in the legs and arms. The plaster paste is molded around the **limb** on top of bandages. It quickly sets into a hard shell, which keeps the bones in place until they heal.
The doctor covered her broken leg with a plaster cast.

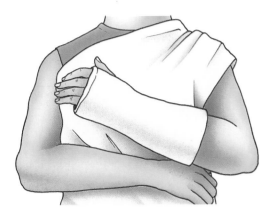

platelet *noun*
Platelets are tiny discs that develop from cells produced in the **bone marrow**. They float in the fluid, or **plasma**, of blood. The billions of platelets in the body help to make the blood **clot**.
When you cut yourself, platelets help to stop the bleeding.

pleura (plural **pleurae**) *noun*
A pleura is one of two layers of **skin** in the **chest**. One layer wraps round the **lung**. The other layer lines the inside of the chest. There is a narrow space between the two layers called the pleural cavity. Fluid in the pleural cavity allows the layers of the pleura to glide past each other every time the lungs move to breathe.
The pleurae are two layers of skin inside the chest cavity.

pleurisy *noun*
Pleurisy is a disorder of one or both **lungs**, when the layers of skin that surround the lungs, or the **pleurae**, become inflamed. Because they are dry and rough, they rub together instead of gliding smoothly past each other. This causes a sharp pain in the chest, which is worse when a person coughs or breathes deeply. Pleurisy is usually a symptom of another illness, such as **pneumonia**.
Pleurisy made it difficult for her to breathe without pain.

pneumonia *noun*
Pneumonia is a disorder of one or both **lungs**. It occurs when harmful germs are breathed into the lungs and start an **infection**. Pneumonia may develop when a person is already ill, very young, or very old. At these times the body's defense against illness, the **immune system**, is weakened. Pneumonia may start with the symptoms of a cold or **influenza**. A person may be breathless, with pain on one side of the chest.
Antibiotic drugs are used to fight lung infections such as pneumonia.

poliomyelitis *noun*
Poliomyelitis is a **disease**. It is carried by a **virus** that attacks **nerves** in the **brain** and **spinal cord**. The virus is **contagious** and can be carried by people with no **symptoms**. The first signs of poliomyelitis are a **fever**, sore **throat**, and **headaches**. A small number of people may then develop a serious form of poliomyelitis with **muscle** pain and a stiff neck. This can lead to **paralysis,** or loss of movement in part or all of the body. Most people recover from the paralysis, but in some cases paralysis may remain.
People can be protected from poliomyelitis by a vaccine given in childhood.

polyp *noun*
A polyp is a lump that forms in moist **skin**. Polyps are usually **benign**, or harmless, but they may cause a blockage. Common places for polyps to grow are in the **nose**, **ear**, **stomach**, and **intestine**. They may also develop in the **uterus**.
Polyps that cause a blockage or become infected may be removed.

pore *noun*
A pore is a tiny opening in the **skin**. **Sweat** passes through pores to the skin's surface.
Washing with cool water helped to close his pores.

posterior *adjective*
Posterior describes the back of any part of the human body. The opposite of posterior is **anterior**, which means front.
The spine is a posterior part of the body.

posture *noun*
Posture is the position of the **body**. Good posture is important when walking, standing, or sitting. The **back** should be straight, **shoulders** relaxed, **head** held up, and **stomach** held in.
Bad posture, with hunched shoulders and a curved back, strains muscles, and causes pain.

pregnancy *noun*
Pregnancy is the time before a baby is born. Pregnancy starts at **conception** and continues until **childbirth**. This lasts about nine months, or 40 weeks. The first sign of pregnancy is a missed period, or time of **menstruation**. After three months, the mother's **abdomen** starts to swell as the **fetus** grows inside the **uterus**.
During the fifth month of her pregnancy, she could feel the baby kicking inside her.

premolar ▶ **tooth**

preventive medicine *noun*
Preventive medicine is a kind of **health** care that tries to prevent illness. **Vaccinations** and regular **check-ups** are two examples. Preventive medicine also teaches people what harms the body, and how to protect it. Learning all about road safety, first aid, and how to live a healthy lifestyle are all kinds of preventive medicine.
Preventive medicine can help people to avoid becoming ill.

probe *noun*
A probe is a thin metal rod with a blunt end. **Doctors** use probes to explore openings in the body, such as a nostril. Probes are also used to look into wounds to find a foreign body, such as a bullet.
The doctor used a probe to unblock the girl's tear duct.

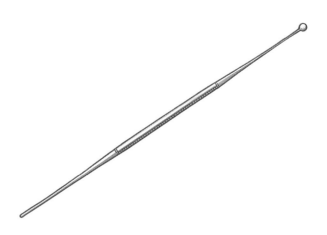

prognosis *noun*
A prognosis is a statement a doctor makes about an illness, including how the illness may develop and what the **patient** can expect to happen. Before a doctor can make a prognosis, he or she must make a **diagnosis**.
The prognosis was that the fever would end in two or three days.

prostaglandin *noun*
Prostaglandin is one of a group of **hormones** found in many tissues and fluids in the body. They activate the body in several different ways. Some kinds of prostaglandin control the acid in the **stomach** juices. Others make the **uterus** contract during **childbirth**. The chemicals in prostaglandins can be used as **medicines.**
Prostaglandins cause a pregnant woman to start labor.

prostate gland *noun*
A prostate gland is a small **organ** in a male. It is the size of a walnut and lies around the **urethra**, the tube that carries **urine** from the **bladder**. The prostate gland releases a fluid that is part of **semen**. In older men, this gland may become enlarged and squeeze the urethra, stopping the flow of urine. When this happens, the prostate gland may be removed in a surgical operation.
The enlarged prostate gland was the reason for his bladder infection.

protein *noun*
Protein is a substance made of **amino acids**. The body needs protein to build and repair **cells**. Different kinds of protein keep **bones**, **blood**, and many other parts of the body healthy. Some proteins are made by the body. Others cannot be made by the body, and need to be eaten in **food**. Meat, fish, eggs, milk, and cheese all contain important proteins the body needs.
Children and pregnant women need to have a diet rich in protein.

psoriasis *noun*
Psoriasis is a disorder of the **skin**. Small silvery scales appear on the skin, with red patches underneath. Sometimes, large areas of psoriasis may cluster on the head, elbows and knees. These areas can be sore, especially when a person is under **stress**, or becomes upset. Psoriasis is not **contagious** and usually runs in families. Sunlight is a good treatment for psoriasis.
The ointment helped to clear up the psoriasis on her elbows.

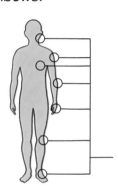

areas of the body where psoriasis usually occurs

psychiatry *noun*
Psychiatry is a branch of medicine that treats mental illness with counseling and sometimes drugs. Doctors who give this kind of medical care are called **psychiatrists**. A psychiatric **hospital** is a place where people who need this kind of care sometimes go to be treated.
The psychiatry students learned how drugs, and other types of therapy might help patients.

puberty *noun*
Puberty is the stage of growth when a child begins to develop into an **adult**. Puberty lasts between two and six years. The glands of the body become very active and produce hormones. During puberty, girls develop **breasts** and start to **menstruate**. The **penis** and **testes** of a boy grow larger and start to produce **semen**, and his voice becomes deeper. Both sexes grow hair under the arms and around the sexual organs.
Puberty can start any time between 11 and 17 years of age.

pubic hair   *noun*
Pubic hair is the thick, short, curly hair that grows around the sexual organs during puberty.
Pubic hair is a sign of puberty.

pubis   *noun*
The pubis is one of two **bones** that form the front ring of the **pelvis**. The pelvis is the circle of bone where the legs meet the rest of the body. The pubic bones curve round the front of the pelvis and meet in the middle.
The bones of the pubis meet at the pubic arch.

puerperal fever   *noun*
Puerperal fever is an infection suffered by women after childbirth.
Thanks to antibiotics, and modern standards of hygiene, puerperal fever is now very rare.

pulmonary   *adjective*
Pulmonary describes anything to do with the **lungs**. **Asthma** is a pulmonary disease.
The mild pulmonary infection could easily have developed into pneumonia.

pulse   *noun*
A pulse is a throb of pressure in the flow of **blood**. The **heart** pumps blood into the arteries, to be carried around the body. The blood flows in a wave every time the heart beats. These surges can be felt as a pulse in the wrist and neck. A pulse that is weak, too fast, or too slow may be a sign of some kind of **illness**.
He was nervous about the interview, so his pulse beat faster.

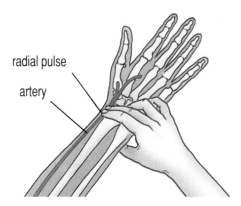

radial pulse

artery

pupil   *noun*
A pupil is the round black opening in the middle of the **iris**, the colored ring of an eye. Light enters the eye through the pupil. The amount of light let in is controlled by **muscles** in the iris, which makes the pupil bigger in dim light and smaller in bright light.
His pupils appeared to grow larger as he moved into the shade.

pus   *noun*
Pus is a thick, yellow or green liquid made by the body. It collects around **infection** in **tissue**. This may cause a painful, red lump, such as an **abscess**. Pus is a sign that the body's defenses, or **immune system**, are at work. Pus is formed from dead **white blood cells,** along with **germs**, dead tissue, and fluid. Pus needs to be drained and cleaned from an infected area.
The wound had become infected, and the bandage was covered with pus.

quarantine *noun*
Quarantine is the period of time that a person with a **contagious disease** must stay away from other people, in order not to pass on the illness.
A yellow flag used to be flown on a boat to show that it was under quarantine.

rabies *noun*
Rabies is a **disease** caused by the bite of an animal infected with the rabies **virus**. Wild animals such as bats, raccoons, and skunks spread the illness. The first signs are a **fever** followed by excited behavior. A person froths at the mouth, the throat closes up and he or she cannot bear to drink water. Someone who has been bitten by an animal with rabies needs medical treatment at once, because once **symptoms** develop, death occurs within a week.
A person who has been exposed to rabies needs to have a series of six injections of vaccine over a one-month period.

radiology *noun*
Radiology is a method of looking inside the body, usually by using **X-rays**. X-rays help doctors to make a **diagnosis**. For example, they can see how a bone is broken or whether there is something wrong with an **organ**. A **scanner** may be used to create pictures of the inside of the body. These pictures can be recorded and analyzed on computers.
Radiology was used to find out whether the rib was broken.

radiotherapy *noun*
Radiotherapy is a way of treating many kinds of **cancer** by using radiation to destroy cancer **cells**. Radiotherapy is often used after an operation to remove a **malignant** growth, or tumor, to kill any cancer cells left behind.
Sometimes, a patient's hair falls out after a course of radiotherapy.

119

radius   *noun*

The radius is the front bone of the forearm. The top end forms part of the **elbow**, and the bottom end is part of the **wrist** joint on the **thumb** side of the hand. The radius can move over and across the **ulna**, the other bone in the forearm. This allows the **palm** of the hand to face up or down by moving the wrist.

Attached to the radius and the ulna are 19 muscles that move the wrist and the fingers.

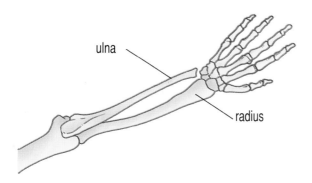

ulna

radius

rash   *noun*

A rash is a skin reaction or infection. Rashes are usually red pimples that itch. The spots may be raised, turn into blisters or break open. Rashes can be caused by a skin irritation or an **allergy**. A rash may also be a **symptom** of an illness, such as measles or chickenpox.

After the boy fell into the poison ivy, he had a rash all over his legs.

rectum   *noun*

The rectum is a tube in the body. It is the end section of the large **intestine** where **feces** are stored. The rectum is about five inches long and reaches from the **colon** to the **anus**. It passes through the **pelvis** and lies behind the **bladder**. When feces fill up the rectum, a person feels the need to have a bowel movement.

The colon is joined to the anus by the rectum.

red blood cell ► **blood cell**

reflex ► page 121

renal   *adjective*

Renal describes anything to do with a **kidney**.

Blood flows into the kidney through the renal artery.

reproduction   *noun*

Reproduction is the process of making **babies**. For reproduction, a **female** and a **male** must be **fertile** and have **sexual intercourse**. **Fertilization** of the ovum is followed by **pregnancy** and **childbirth**.

Without reproduction, the human race would die out.

reproductive   *adjective*

respiration ► page 122

retina   *noun*

The retina is the layer of special **cells** that lines the back of an eyeball. Light is focused onto the retina through the **lens**. Cells called **rods** pick up light and other cells called **cones** pick up color. The messages of light and color are sent along the **optic nerve** to the **brain**.

Damage to the retina can sometimes cause blindness.

rheumatic fever   *noun*

Rheumatic fever is a **disease** most often found in children between 5 and 15 years of age. Rheumatic fever is caused by an unusual reaction to a throat infection. Two weeks after a sore throat, the joints become swollen and painful. There may be a fever, rash, and pains in the chest and stomach.

Most people recover completely from rheumatic fever, although a serious attack may damage the heart.

rheumatism   *noun*

Rheumatism is pain, stiffness, and **inflammation** in muscles and joints. Many elderly people suffer from rheumatism.

His rheumatism was relieved by aspirin.

reflex *noun*

A reflex is an automatic response made by the body. This can be a **movement**, as in a **motor** reflex. Other kinds of reflex action can develop through memory. The brain remembers how to respond to certain signals or situations. This is called a conditioned reflex. Hearing an icecream van might make someone's mouth water. This is a conditioned reflex.

Blinking when something suddenly comes too close to the eyes is a motor reflex.

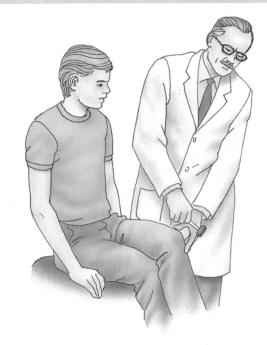

Doctors test the knee reflex to make sure the nervous system is intact. To test the knee reflex, the patient sits with one knee crossed over the other. The doctor taps the knee just below the kneecap.

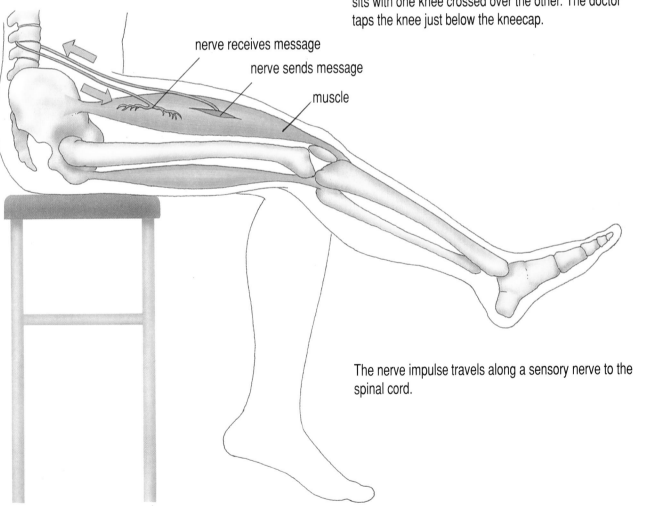

nerve receives message

nerve sends message

muscle

The nerve impulse travels along a sensory nerve to the spinal cord.

respiration   *noun*

Respiration is the process by which the body obtains **oxygen** and gets rid of a waste gas called **carbon dioxide**. Humans obtain oxygen by breathing air. Air is drawn in to the **lungs**, where oxygen is taken into the **blood** and circulated to every **cell** in the body. Carbon dioxide leaves the body when a person breathes out.

During respiration, an adult breathes 15 or 20 times a minute.

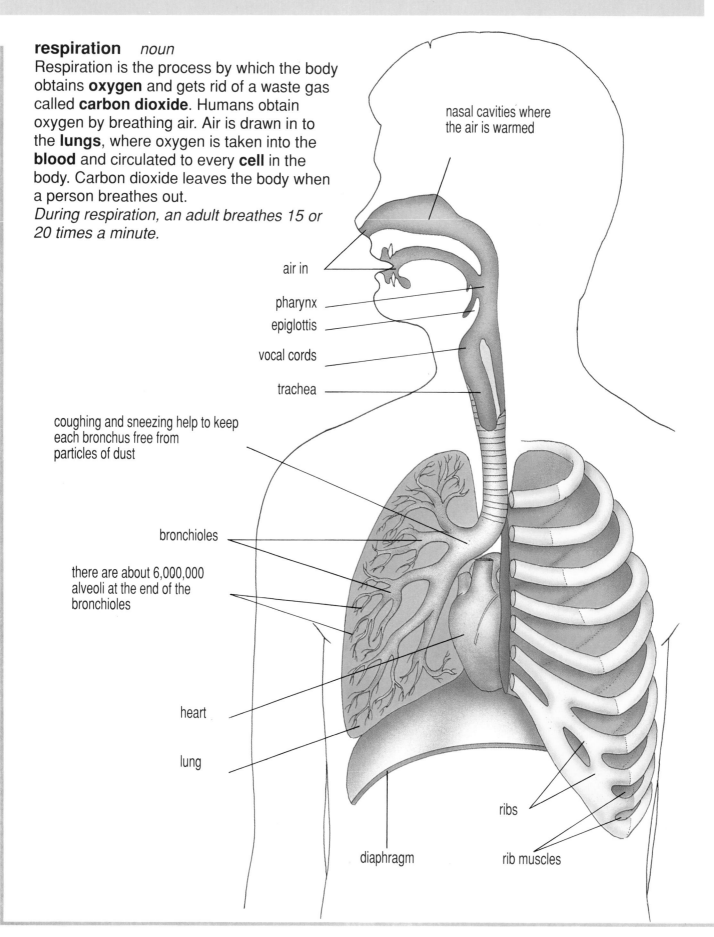

nasal cavities where the air is warmed

air in

pharynx

epiglottis

vocal cords

trachea

coughing and sneezing help to keep each bronchus free from particles of dust

bronchioles

there are about 6,000,000 alveoli at the end of the bronchioles

heart

lung

diaphragm

ribs

rib muscles

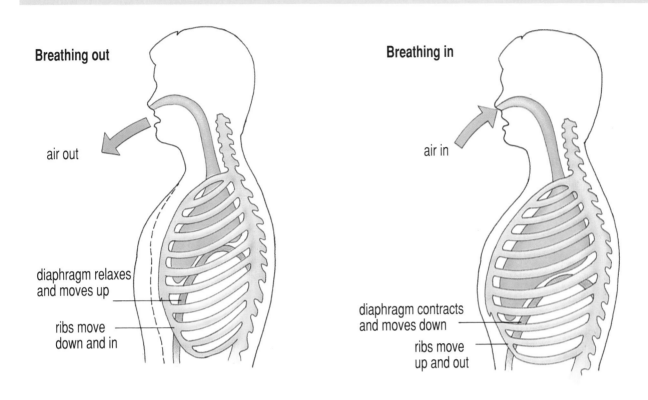

Breathing out

air out

diaphragm relaxes
and moves up

ribs move
down and in

Breathing in

air in

diaphragm contracts
and moves down

ribs move
up and out

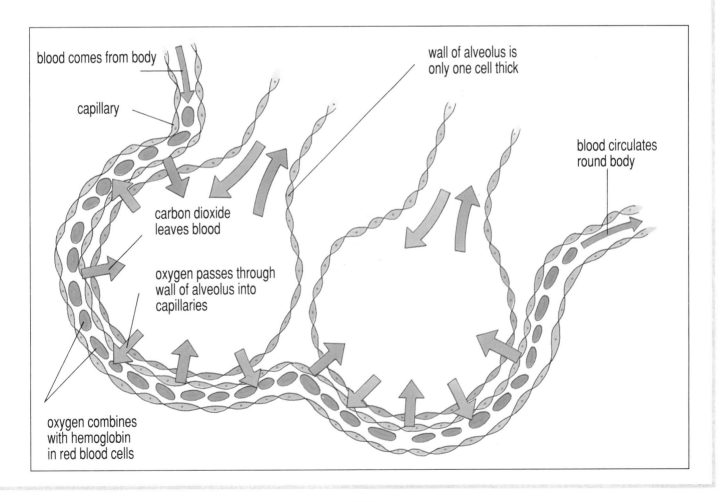

blood comes from body

capillary

wall of alveolus is
only one cell thick

blood circulates
round body

carbon dioxide
leaves blood

oxygen passes through
wall of alveolus into
capillaries

oxygen combines
with hemoglobin
in red blood cells

rib noun
A rib is a thin, curved **bone** in the **chest**. There are 12 pairs of ribs in the body. Each pair of ribs is joined to the **spine** at the back. The first seven pairs join the **breastbone** at the front. Three more pairs are connected to the breastbone with **cartilage**. The last two pairs curve only half way around and are called floating ribs.
The ribs form a cage to protect the organs in the chest.

rickets *noun*
Rickets is a **disease** that occurs when children do not get enough **vitamin** D. Rickets prevents the bones from growing properly and makes them soft. The skin makes vitamin D when a person is in sunlight. It is also found in some foods, such as fish and eggs. Rickets is treated with supplements of vitamin D and calcium.
Cheese is rich in vitamin D, and can help to prevent rickets.

rod ► **eye**

root canal *noun*
A root canal is the passage through the root of a **tooth**. Root canals connect the soft pulp inside teeth with nerves and a supply of blood. If the inside of a tooth dies, the root canal must be cleaned and filled by a **dentist**.
He needed root canal surgery to treat his toothache.

rubella *noun*
Rubella is a **contagious disease**, caused by a **virus**. It is often called German measles. The symptoms of rubella are a **headache**, **fever**, and sore throat followed by a **rash** of small red spots. Rubella is contagious from a week before until five days after the rash appears. If rubella is caught by a woman in the first three months of pregnancy, it can harm the baby she is carrying.
Children are usually vaccinated against rubella so they will never catch the disease.

sac *noun*
A sac is a pouch of **tissue**. Sacs line hollows or surround spaces in the body. They may also contain fluid, organs, or other tissue. There are many kinds of sacs in the body, such as the tiny air sacs in the lungs called **alveoli**.
The scrotal sac contains a man's testes.

sacro- *prefix*
Sacro- is a prefix that refers to anything to do with the **sacrum**.
The sacroiliac joint connects the sacrum to the ilium.

sacrum *noun*
The sacrum is part of a **spine**. It is five bones, or **vertebrae**, of the lower back fused into one triangular shape. The sacrum forms the back part of the **pelvis**, with the hipbones on either side. The bottom of the sacrum joins the tailbone, or the **coccyx**. This part of the pelvis takes the weight of the body from the rest of the spine.
Cartilage connects the sacrum to the coccyx.

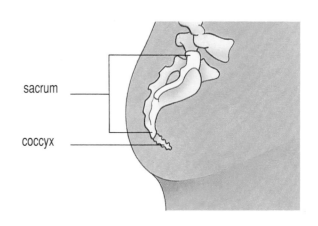

sacrum

coccyx

saline *noun*
Saline is a fluid made by mixing a tiny amount of a salt called sodium chloride in water. This makes a fluid very like the fluid called **plasma**, in blood. Saline can be injected into the body to replace plasma.
After the operation, the patient was connected to a saline drip.

saliva *noun*
Saliva is a watery fluid made by the **salivary glands** in the mouth. Saliva mixes with **food** to make it easier to swallow. The **enzyme** and salts in saliva start to break down food as it enters the mouth. Saliva enables people to taste flavors in food and helps to keep the mouth clean.
The sight of the chocolate cake made his mouth fill with saliva.

salivary gland *noun*
A salivary gland releases a fluid called **saliva**. There are three main pairs of salivary glands in the mouth. These are inside the cheeks, at the back of the mouth, and under the tongue.
The salivary glands beneath the tongue are known as the sublingual glands.

salmonella *noun*
Salmonella is a **bacterium**. If a person eats food infected with salmonella, he or she becomes ill within two days. The bacteria travel to the **intestine** and cause pain, vomiting, and diarrhea. People with salmonella poisoning need to drink plenty of fluids and see a doctor.
Salmonella poisoning can be serious in young children and elderly people.

sarcoma *noun*
A sarcoma is a type of **cancer** that occurs in **connective tissue** such as **cartilage**, **muscle**, or **bone**. The growths are **malignant**, and can spread to other parts of the body. Sarcomas are usually treated by being surgically removed.
Sarcomas are much less common than carcinomas.

scab *noun*
A scab is a hard crust of dried **blood** and **pus**. Scabs form over a scratch, cut, or sore and protect the **skin** underneath while it is healing. Scabs fall off when the skin has healed.
A scab is also called a blood clot.

scabies *noun*
Scabies is a **skin infection** caused by a tiny mite that burrows under the skin. This makes the skin break out in a red, pimply **rash** with a burning itch. Common places for scabies are the hands and around the sexual organs. The scabies mite is easily passed by touching an infected person.
Scabies is an example of a contagious disease.

scabies mite

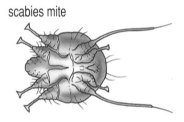

scald *noun*
A scald is a **burn** caused by hot liquid or vapor, such as boiling water or steam.
She plunged her hand into cold water to stop the scald from becoming worse.

scalp *noun*
The scalp is the covering of **skin** and **hair** that protects the **skull**. The layer of **muscle** and other **tissue** underneath this area of skin is also part of the scalp.
Head lice made the girl's scalp itch.

scan *noun*
A scan is a way of looking inside the body. A machine called a **scanner** uses radiation, sound, or magnetic forces to form an image of the **organs** inside the body, because all these forces are able to pass through the skin. Computers linked to the scanner are able to display the images on a screen, or copy them onto paper.
A scan was done to see if he had gallstones.

125

scanner *noun*
A scanner is a machine that makes a **scan**, or a picture of the body inside the skin. Scanners use sound, radiation, or magnetic forces that can pass through the body without hurting any part of it. They are linked to computers which build up pictures of every part of an **organ**. An **ultrasound** scanner is able to display a picture of a baby inside a pregnant woman on a computer screen.
The scanner could show whether the fetus was developing properly.

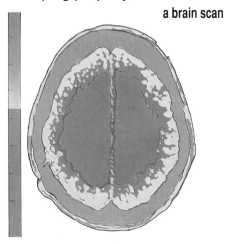

a brain scan

scapula (plural **scapulae**) *noun*
The scapula, or **shoulder** blade, is a flat triangle of **bone** that forms the back of the shoulder joint. The **collarbone** links the scapula to the **sternum** at the front of the body. Muscles attached to the scapula help the arm and shoulder to move.
As the girl moved her arm, her scapula moved with it.

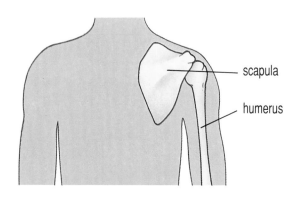

scapula
humerus

scar *noun*
A scar is the mark left after a **wound** heals. Scars from most small injuries heal and fade to a thin, white line. Scars that form into thick, red, lumpy **tissue** can usually be removed by surgery.
He had a long scar on his arm where he fell on the glass.

scarlet fever *noun*
Scarlet fever is a childhood **disease**. It is **infectious** and spreads easily from one child to another. The first signs are a sudden fever and sore throat, headache, vomiting, and diarrhea. A fine pink **rash** spreads all over the body from the neck and chest. The tongue is coated white and also covered in red spots. The symptoms may last for only a few days, although a person may still be infectious for three weeks.
Scarlet fever is treated with a course of antibiotics.

schistosomiasis ▶ bilharzia

scrotum *noun*
The scrotum is the loose bag of skin that contains a man's **testes**. It hangs below the **penis**, between the legs. During **puberty,** the testes enlarge and drop lower and the scrotum gets bigger. **Muscles** in the scrotum pull the testes up toward the body when it is cold and relax to drop them away from the body when it is hot, in order to keep the **sperm** inside at the proper temperature.
The epididymis is also located in the scrotum.

scurvy *noun*
Scurvy is a **disease** that occurs when a person does not have enough **vitamin** C in the diet. Vitamin C is found in fresh fruits and vegetables. The first sign of scurvy is swollen, bleeding **gums**, followed by bleeding under the skin. This may lead to a blood disorder called **anemia**.
People with scurvy soon recover after adding vitamin C to a balanced diet of food.

seasickness   *noun*
Seasickness is a kind of motion sickness caused by the rocking of a boat on the sea. The movements upset the organs of **balance**, or **semi-circular canals**, in the **ear**. Someone with seasickness feels nauseous, and **vomits**. There are medicines that can be taken before a journey that help prevent seasickness.
Children often grow out of seasickness.

sebaceous gland   *noun*
A sebaceous gland is a part of **skin**. These tiny glands open into **hair follicles** and release an oily substance called **sebum**.
A blocked sebaceous gland can become infected and swell up like a boil.

sebum   *noun*
Sebum is a thick, oily substance. It is made by the **sebaceous glands** that surround and feed each hair root. Sebum is released into the **hair follicles** under the **skin**.
Sebum helps to keep hair soft and clean.

secrete   *verb*
To secrete is to release a substance. **Glands** in the body, such as salivary glands, secrete fluids through tubes. Some substances are also secreted straight into the **bloodstream**, such as **hormones** from the **ovaries**. Any substance or fluid made and secreted by a gland is called a secretion.
A very nervous person secretes sweat from the palms of the hands.
secretion   *noun*

semen   *noun*
Semen is a thick, creamy fluid. It is made in the male's body from **puberty** onward, and is released through the **penis**. Each release of semen consists of only about two teaspoonfuls of liquid, but this contains millions of **sperm** that are capable of fertilizing eggs. Semen is an essential part of **reproduction** and **sexual intercourse.**
The sperm in man's semen are necessary to fertilize a woman's ovum.

semicircular canal   *noun*
The semicircular canals are three tubes filled with fluid in the **inner ear**. These tubes are arranged as loops that join to the rest of the inner ear, or the **cochlea**. Semicircular canals are the main organs of **balance**. The fluid in the loops moves as the body moves and sends a message to the **brain**. The brain then instructs the body to move in the right way to maintain its balance.
Infection in the semicircular canal can make you dizzy.

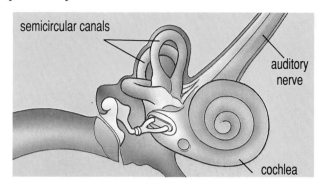
semicircular canals
auditory nerve
cochlea

sense   *noun*
The five senses are sight, hearing, touch, taste, and smell. The **eyes**, **ears**, **skin**, **mouth**, and **nose** are the sense organs.
He used his sense of smell to tell what kind of flower it was.

sensory nerve ▶ **nerve ending**

septic   *adjective*
Septic describes an infection that forms **pus**. This is caused by germs invading the body, often through a cut or wound in the **skin**.
The opposite of septic is antiseptic.

septicemia   *noun*
Septicemia is a **blood disease** that occurs when germs get into the **bloodstream** and poison the blood. This may cause infections, such as **abscesses**, in any part of the body. The first signs of septicemia are red streaks leading away from a wound on the skin, along with fever and chills.
A person with septicemia needs medical treatment at once.

127

skeleton   *noun*

The skeleton is the framework of all the **bones** in the body. There are over 200 bones in an adult skeleton. These are all linked by **joints** and held in place by **ligaments**. **Tendons** attach layers of **muscle** to the bones. Muscles control all the moving parts of a skeleton. The skeleton supports the body and protects all the **organs** inside.

A baby's skeleton contains about 350 bones, many of which fuse together as the baby grows.

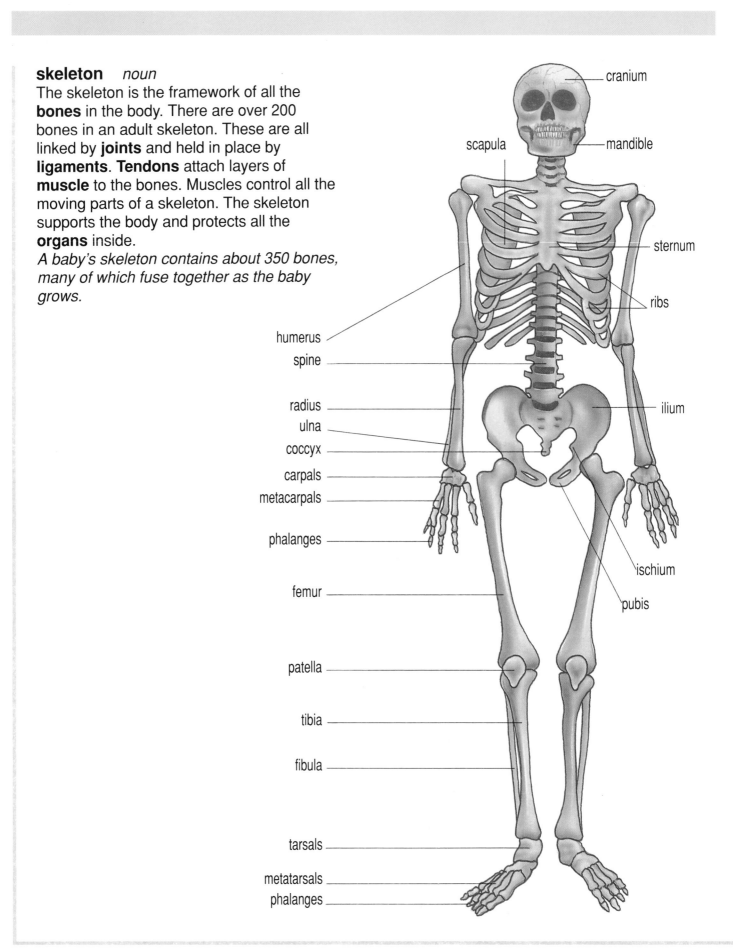

cranium

scapula

mandible

sternum

ribs

humerus

spine

radius

ilium

ulna

coccyx

carpals

metacarpals

phalanges

ischium

femur

pubis

patella

tibia

fibula

tarsals

metatarsals

phalanges

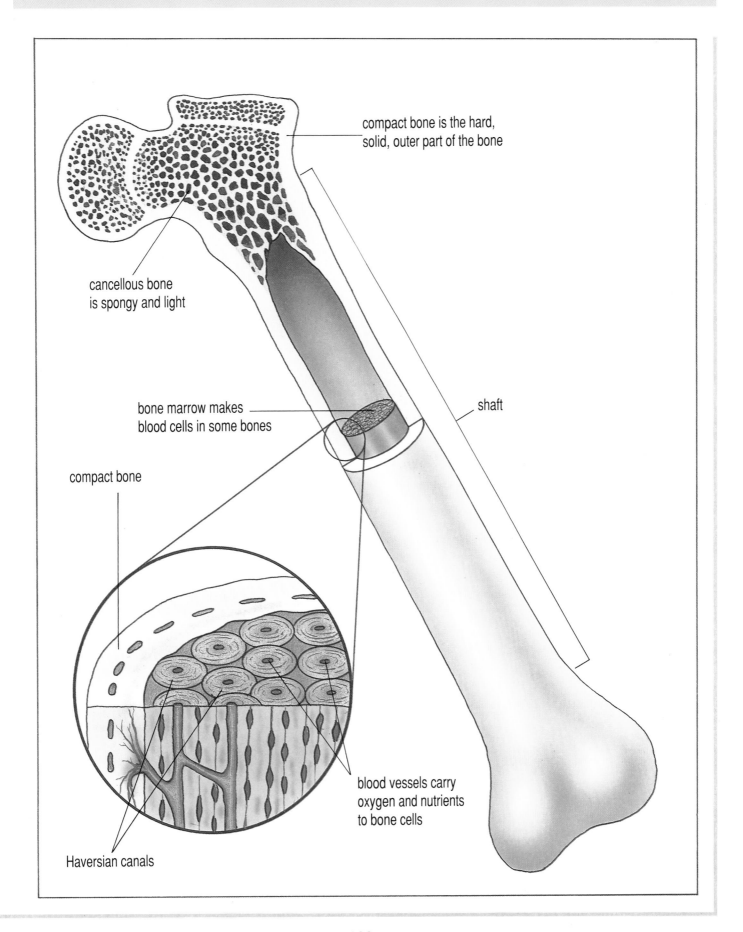

compact bone is the hard,
solid, outer part of the bone

cancellous bone
is spongy and light

bone marrow makes
blood cells in some bones

shaft

compact bone

blood vessels carry
oxygen and nutrients
to bone cells

Haversian canals

septum (plural **septa**) *noun*
A septum is a wall of thin **tissue**. Septa divide one part of an organ from another, such as the septum in the **nose** that separates the two nostrils. Other septa in the body include those that divide the chambers of the **heart**, the **lobes** of the **brain**, and the two halves of the **scrotum**.
She was born with a hole in the septum of her heart.
septal *adjective*

serum (plural **sera**) *noun*
Serum is part of **blood**. It is the clear fluid that is left after a blood **clot** forms. Serum is similar to **plasma**, the other fluid in blood, but it does not contain the substances that make blood clot. Some types of serum can be used to treat disease or poisoning.
The explorers took plenty of snake bite serum with them.
serous *adjective*

sex *noun*
Sex refers to whether a person is **male** or **female**. The sex of a baby is decided at conception, and depends on which types of **chromosome** are present in the sperm and egg that join together.
Nowadays medical tests can determine the sex of a baby before it is born.
sexual *adjective*

sexual intercourse *noun*
Sexual intercourse is a part of **reproduction**. The sexual **organs** of a man and a woman meet during sexual intercourse, and **semen** is released from the penis. **Sperm** in the semen swim up into the **uterus** and the **Fallopian tubes**. If a sperm fertilizes an **ovum**, **conception** takes place.
Sexual intercourse is the way human beings reproduce.

shiatsu *noun*
Shiatsu is a method of massaging the body by finger pressure. It originated in Japan.
Shiatsu can relieve aches and pains.

shin *noun*
The shin is the front part of each leg, from the **knee** to the **ankle**.
During a soccer match, the players are often kicked in the shin.

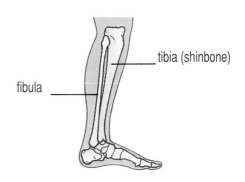

tibia (shinbone)

fibula

shinbone ► **tibia**

shivering *noun*
Shivering is the way the body shakes and trembles when it is very cold. If the **jaw** shivers, the **teeth** 'chatter' or clack together and make a noise. Shivering is caused by **muscles** that tighten, or contract, very quickly, one after the other. This helps to warm the body if a person is cold, has a shock, or feels afraid.
She stopped shivering after she went inside and stood next to the radiator.
shiver *verb*

shock *noun*
Shock is an illness that causes the **blood pressure** to drop so that not enough blood circulates around the body. Shock may occur when a person loses a great deal of blood, has an accident, or a severe emotional upset. It can also be a **symptom** of another illness. A person with shock has cold, moist, pale skin, a weak and rapid **pulse**, a dry mouth, and an unusual breathing rate. Shock needs to be treated by a doctor as soon as possible.
Everyone involved in the car crash had to be treated for shock.

short-sightedness ► **myopia**

shoulder *noun*

The shoulder joins the **arm** to the rest of the body. Each shoulder has a ball and socket **joint** where the bones meet. The shoulder joint is between the upper arm bone, or **humerus**, and the shoulder blade, or **scapula**. The **collarbone** supports the front of the shoulder. Strong **muscles** and **ligaments** hold the shoulder in place and allow it to move in all directions.
His shoulder ached from throwing the ball so much.

sight *noun*

Sight is a **sense**. It is being able to see light, color, shape, and size through the **eyes**, the organs of sight. An object is seen at a slightly different angle by each eye, and the **brain** makes one complete picture of the object using the information from both eyes. This is called stereoscopic vision and is the reason that the world looks three-dimensional. Lack of sight is called **blindness**.
Sight usually gets worse as a person ages.

sinew ► tendon

sinus *noun*

A sinus is a space, or **cavity,** in the body. The sinuses in the **skull** are lined with a moist skin and lie in the bone behind the nose. These air-filled spaces help to make the skull lighter in weight. They act as echo chambers for the **voice**. Sinuses also warm the air breathed in through the **nose**.
When sinuses become blocked, it is difficult to breathe.

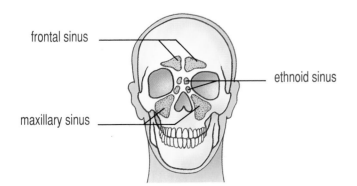

frontal sinus

maxillary sinus

ethnoid sinus

skeleton ► page 128

skin ► page 132

skin blemish *noun*

Skin blemishes are small, inflamed **swellings** on the **skin** that occur when the openings, or **pores**, in the skin become blocked. **Sebum**, the oil made by the skin, builds up behind the blockage, and the skin becomes inflamed. Squeezing skin blemishes can let in **germs** and cause **infection**. People often have skin blemishes during **puberty** because the skin makes more oil during this time. Skin blemishes are also called spots or pimples.
Her mother told her not to touch her skin blemishes.

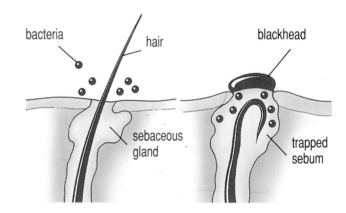

bacteria

hair

blackhead

sebaceous gland

trapped sebum

skull *noun*

The skull is the bony box that forms the **head**. It is also called the cranium and is made up of 22 **bones**. The part of the skull that covers the **brain** is made from strong, flat bones shaped like a helmet. The bones of the **face** have hollows for the eyes, nose, and ears. The only bone of the skull that moves is the **jawbone**.
The bones in a newborn baby's skull are separated by cartilage.

sleep ► page 134

skin *noun*

Skin is the outer covering of the body. It is made of tough **tissue** and protects the inside of the body from germs and injury. The outer layer of skin is called the **epidermis**. The middle layer is called the **dermis**. The inner **subcutaneous** layer contains fat. Hair, sweat, and blood vessels in the skin help to keep the body at the right **temperature**. Skin also contains nerve cells that send messages of heat, cold, and pain to the brain.

The skin is the largest organ in the body.

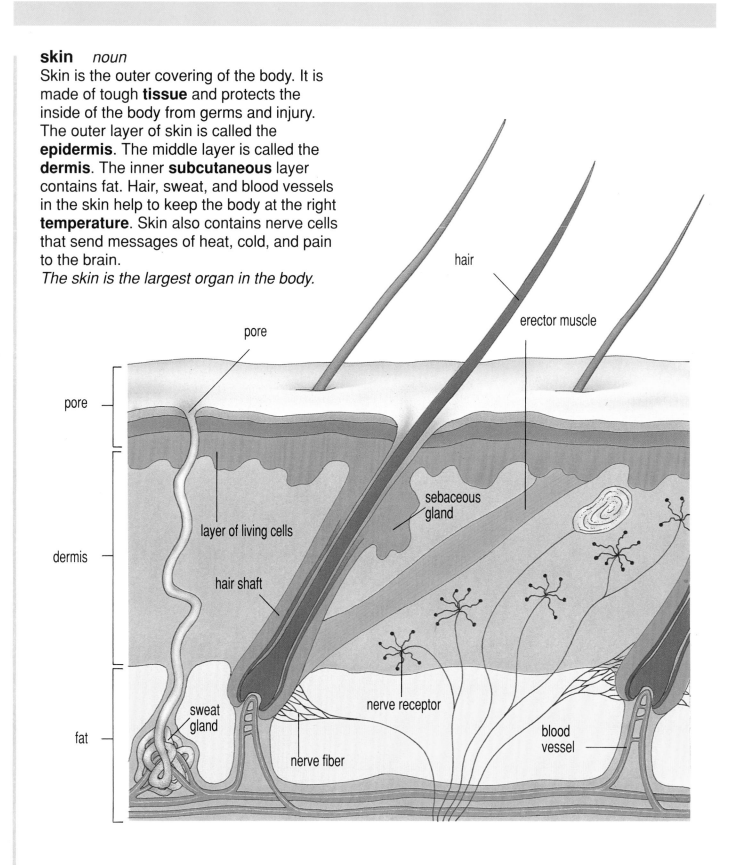

To cool down

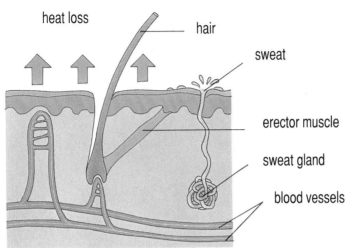

To warm up

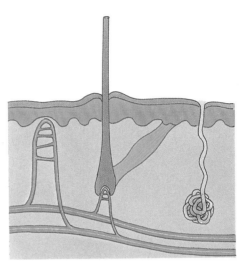

Blood vessels widen in order to carry more blood near the skin's surface. Heat is given off. Hairs lie flat to ensure no air is trapped between them. Sweat glands produce more sweat. Sweat contains water, salts and other waste matter. Sweat evaporates when it reaches the surface of the skin, cooling the body.

Blood vessels near the surface of the skin become narrower. Blood flows through blood vessels that lie deeper under the skin. Little heat is lost. Erector muscles contract to make hair stand on end. This traps warm air between the hairs to act as insulation. The skin has goose-pimples.

Fingerprints

No two people in the world have exactly identical fingerprints. The patterns on the skin remain the same throughout a person's life. Fingerprints are formed by ridges in the epidermis.

133

sleep *noun*
Sleep is a time of rest during which a person is not conscious. During sleep, the **heartbeat** and the **breathing** slow down, and the **muscles** relax. Sleep restores **energy** to the body and the **brain**. Most adults sleep for about seven or eight hours a night. Most people have periods of light and deep sleep. People **dream** while they sleep, but often do not remember their dreams. *Growing children need more sleep than adults.*

Waves of electrical activity in the brain can be measured by an electroencephalograph machine. The machine prints out the activity as a pattern.

During deep sleep, the eyes remain still. The body is relaxed. Brain waves are large and slow.

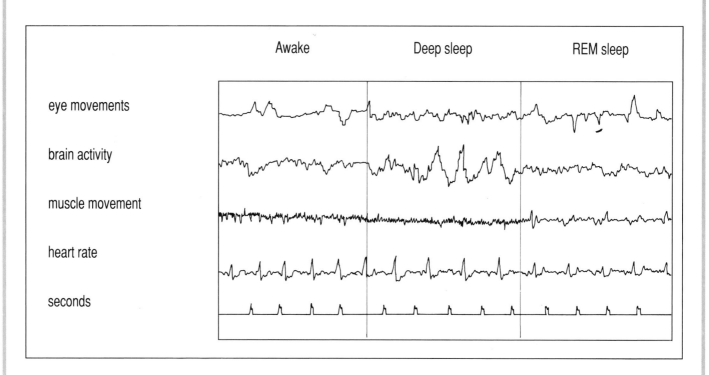

	Awake	Deep sleep	REM sleep
eye movements			
brain activity			
muscle movement			
heart rate			
seconds			

People dream during light, or Rapid Eye Movement (REM), sleep. The eyes flicker under the eyelids. REM brain activity shows smaller, faster waves, in a pattern similar to that when awake.

A sleeping body changes position at least twelve times during a night's sleep.

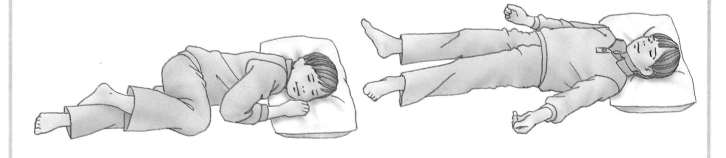

sleeping sickness *noun*
Sleeping sickness is a **disease** found in Africa. It is caused by the bite of a tsetse fly carrying the sleeping sickness **germ**. Two weeks after a bite, **fever** and swollen glands develop. The germs eventually attack the brain. A person then becomes very sleepy, falls into a coma, and usually dies.
Sleeping sickness can be cured if treated before the brain is affected.

small intestine *noun*
The small intestine is part of the **digestive system**. It is over 20 feet long and coiled inside the **abdomen**. This tube is divided into three parts called the **duodenum**, **jejunum** and **ileum**.
Enzymes secreted by the small intestine help to digest food.

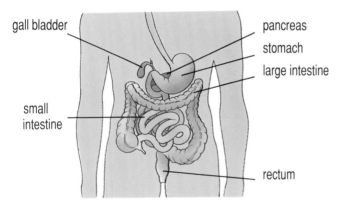

gall bladder
pancreas
stomach
large intestine
small intestine
rectum

smallpox *noun*
Smallpox is a **disease** caused by a **virus**. The **symptoms** are a **fever** and **rash** of red **pimples** over the body, which fill with **pus** and form **scabs**. **Scars** are left behind after the scabs have fallen off. Due to vaccination, smallpox has been virtually wiped out around the world.
Many people died or were left scarred through smallpox.

smear *noun*
A smear is a small amount of tissue or other substance that is put on a slide for examination under a microscope.
The smear showed that she had an infection.

smell *noun*
Smell is a sense. It is being able to pick up different scents in the air, such as the smell of food. Special cells in the back of the **nose** send the message of smells to the **brain**. The **cerebrum** is the part of the brain that controls smell. Most animals have a better sense of smell than humans, who can only pick up seven main kinds of scents.
Dogs have an excellent sense of smell.

sneeze *noun*
A sneeze is a **reflex action** in which a sudden gust of air is blown out of the **mouth** and **nose** with great force. This happens when dust or any other substance irritates the moist skin inside the nose. A sneeze is the body's way of cleaning out the passages of the nose.
The loud sneeze startled everyone.

socket *noun*
A socket is a hollow shape that fits around a ball shape. The **legs** and **arms** join the rest of the body with a ball and socket **joint**, in which the ball end of one bone fits into the socket end of another. The **eyeballs** fit into sockets in the **skull** called **orbits**.
A dislocated bone is one that has come out of its socket.

solar plexus *noun*
The solar plexus is a network of **nerves** that lies at the back of the **abdomen** behind the **stomach**. Nerves from the solar plexus branch out to the rest of the body.
A hard blow to the solar plexus is painful.

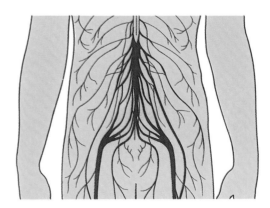

spasm *noun*

A spasm is a sudden, involuntary movement of a **muscle**, or group of muscles. The muscle suddenly tightens and stays taut, and the part of the body seized by a spasm locks into a stiff position.

A spasm may be a simple cramp or it may be a sign of illness.

speech *noun*

Speech is the act of speaking. The sounds of speech are made in the **larynx**, and formed by different movements of the **tongue**, **lips** and **jaws**. The part of the brain responsible for speech is the **cerebrum**.

His speech was slurred because he was very tired.

sperm *noun*

A sperm is a male **sex** cell. Millions of sperm are made in the **testes** and released through the **penis** in **semen**. Each sperm has a head, a neck, and a tail. When sperm are released in a woman's body, they swim up into the **uterus** and **Fallopian tubes**. If one sperm meets a female **ovum**, both cells join together and **fertilization** takes place.

A sperm looks like a tiny tadpole.

sphincter *noun*

A sphincter is a strong ring of **muscle** that is able to open and close an opening in the body. The sphincter in the **anus** allows **feces** to pass out of the body.

Sphincter muscles close the opening from the bladder to the urethra.

spina bifida *noun*

Spina bifida is a disorder of the **spine**. It is a **congenital** disorder, which means that a person is born with it. Babies that are born with spina bifida may have one or more **vertebrae** missing from their spine. Part of the **spinal cord** sometimes sticks out of the spinal column. When the spinal cord is damaged, spina bifida causes **paralysis** in the legs.

Spina bifida can be detected before a baby is born.

spinal cord *noun*

The spinal cord is part of the **nervous system**. It is the dense bundle of **nerves** that runs down the middle of the spine from the **brain**. Nerves in the spinal cord branch out and connect the brain with every part of the body. Messages to and from the body travel through the spinal cord.

If the spinal cord is damaged, paralysis can result.

spinal nerve *noun*

The spinal nerves are the nerves that form the **spinal cord**. There are 31 pairs of spinal nerves that branch out from the **spine** to the rest of the body. Each nerve is joined to the spinal cord by two roots. The front root is a **motor nerve**. This carries messages from the **brain** to the **muscles** and tells them to move. The back root is a **sensory nerve**. This receives messages from the body and sends them to the brain.

Each pair of spinal nerves corresponds with one of the vertebrae.

spine ▶ page 137

spleen *noun*

A spleen is an **organ** in the **abdomen**. It lies above and behind the **stomach**, under the ribs on the left side. The spleen is made of spongy **tissue** and it stores blood that can be used if there is a sudden loss of blood in the body. The spleen also makes **white blood cells**, which are part of the body's defense, or **immune system.**

The spleen is about the size of an adult's fist.

spondylosis *noun*

Spondylosis is a disorder of the **spine**. It is a kind of weakening and collapse that affects the **vertebrae** and the **discs** between them. Spondylosis in the **neck** causes aching and stiffness. There may be a grating sound when a person turns the neck. Spondylosis in the lower back causes backache and muscle **spasm**.

She had a stiff back due to spondylosis.

spine *noun*

The spine is the backbone of the body. Bones called **vertebrae** sit on top of each other from the neck down to the lower back. Each vertebra is cushioned by strong discs of **cartilage** and held in place with **ligaments** and **muscles**. These allow the spine to twist and bend. The vertebrae are shaped like rings, and surround and protect the **spinal cord**.

The skull rests on the top vertebra in the spine.

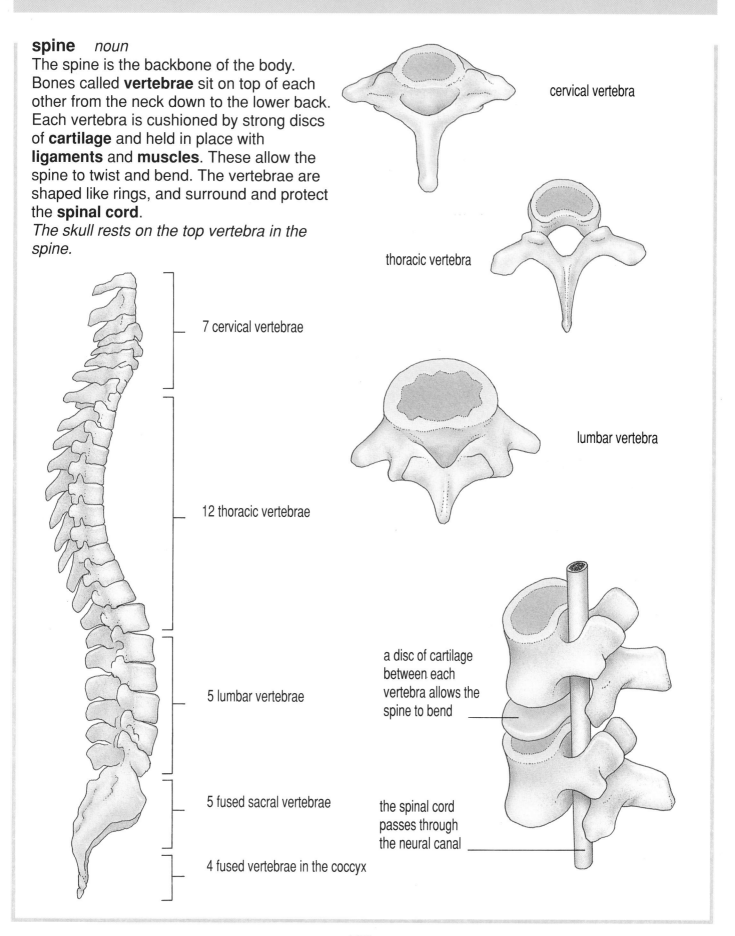

cervical vertebra

thoracic vertebra

lumbar vertebra

7 cervical vertebrae

12 thoracic vertebrae

5 lumbar vertebrae

5 fused sacral vertebrae

4 fused vertebrae in the coccyx

a disc of cartilage between each vertebra allows the spine to bend

the spinal cord passes through the neural canal

spot ► **skin blemish**

sprain *noun*
A sprain is an injury to a **joint**. Sprains occur when the strong strips of **tissue**, or **ligaments**, that hold joints in place are over-stretched or torn. Sprains are painful and make the tissue around the joint swell. A sprained joint must be rested until it heals.
The skin around a sprain may turn black and blue.

stamina *noun*
Stamina, or endurance, is a measure of **fitness.** Good stamina enables a person to keep up an activity for a long time without getting tired. People build up stamina by taking regular **exercise**. The **heart**, **lungs**, and **muscles** become stronger and give the body staying power. Building up stamina is an important part of a healthy lifestyle.
To run a marathon, a person must have enormous stamina.

stammer ► **stutter**

starch *noun*
Starch is a type of carbohydrate and is found in foods, such as bread, cereals, and potatoes. Carbohydrates are one of the important parts of a balanced diet. The starch in food is broken down in the body and used as **energy**.
Iodine can be used to test for the presence of starch in food.

sterile *adjective*
1. Sterile describes a person who is unable to have children. Another word for sterile is infertile. The opposite of sterile is **fertile.**
Certain kinds of disease can make people sterile.
2. Sterile also describes something that is free from bacteria and viruses, and completely clean.
The nurse applied a sterile bandage to the wound.
sterility *noun*

sterilize *verb*
To sterilize something is to kill all the **germs** living on it. The instruments that doctors use on patients are sterilized. This is to prevent germs from getting into the body and causing **infection**. People sterilize areas with chemicals such as **antiseptics**, and **disinfectants**. Objects can also be sterilized with boiling water or steam, as heat kills germs.
Bandages have to be sterilized before they are sold.
sterilization *noun*

sternum *noun*
The sternum is a **bone** that runs down the middle of the **chest**. This flat bone is shaped like a dagger. The **collarbones** join the handle of the dagger at the top of the sternum. The first seven pairs of **ribs** curve round and join the blade as it narrows down to a point. The sternum moves in and out with the ribcage as a person breathes. It helps to protect the **heart** and **lungs** inside.
Another name for the sternum is the breastbone.

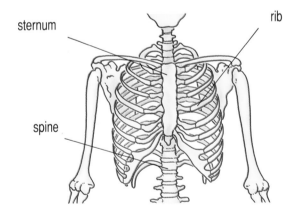

steroid *noun*
A steroid is a kind of **chemical** substance. Many of the **hormones** made by the body are steroids. Steroids can also be made artificially. These kinds of steroid are used as medicines to treat some kinds of illness.
Athletes can be banned from sports if they take steroids.

138

stethoscope *noun*
A stethoscope is an instrument that **doctors** and **nurses** use to listen to sounds inside the body. One end is a disk that is pressed against the skin. Two tubes connect the disk to a pair of curved ends that fit into the doctor's ears. Sounds inside the body are picked up by the disk and travel through the tubes to the ears.
The stethoscope is used to listen to the heart and lungs.

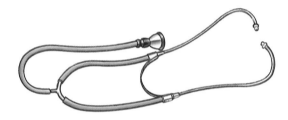

stiffness *noun*
Stiffness is a **symptom**. It means not being able to bend **joints** or flex **muscles** easily. Stiff muscles and joints are sometimes painful. Exercise and massage are good treatments for muscle stiffness.
The old man found it difficult to climb the stairs because of the stiffness in his knees.

stimulate *verb*
To stimulate is to start or increase action in the body. Most parts of the body react when they are stimulated. Light and sound stimulate eyes and ears. Some **drugs** contain stimulants that activate **organs** in the body.
Caffeine, found in coffee, stimulates the central nervous system.
stimulant *noun*

stirrup *noun*
A stirrup is one of three tiny **bones** in the **middle ear** called the **ossicles**. The other bones are called the **anvil** and the **hammer**. They are all shaped like their names. The ossicles pick up sound waves and pass them on to the **inner ear**.
The stirrup is the smallest bone in the human body.

stomach *noun*
A stomach is an **organ** in the upper part of the **abdomen**. Food and liquid enter the stomach from the **esophagus**. Strong **muscles** in the stomach mash up the food, and **acids** in the stomach help to break it up. Some parts of the food, such as **glucose**, are absorbed into the blood through the stomach walls.
Food passes into the duodenum from the stomach.

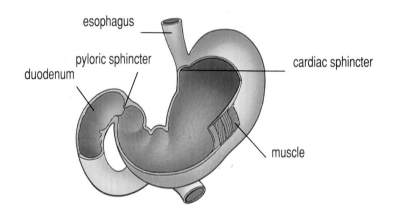

stone *noun*
A stone is a small, hard lump that forms in the body. Stones are made of **minerals** and **salts** that collect in hollow **organs** or tubes. If they cause a blockage, stones need to be removed or dissolved. Common places for stones to form are in the **gall bladder** and **kidneys.**
Some stones can be dissolved within the body by using sound waves.

strength *noun*
Strength is the power of the body. How strong a person is depends on the strength of his or her **muscles** and **bones**. Bodies become strong with regular **exercise**. Strength also develops when a person eats a balanced **diet** and has the right amount of **sleep** and rest. Building up strength is an important part of a healthy **lifestyle.**
It took her a long time to regain her strength after her illness.
strong *adjective*

stress *noun*

Stress is a tension in the mind and body that can cause **illness**. It occurs when the body or mind is given too much to do. Stress makes a person worried and anxious. When a person feels stress, he or she has a faster **heartbeat** and higher **blood pressure**, which can lead to illness. The best treatment for stress is learning how to relax. Exercise and meditation are often recommended to help relieve stress.

People often suffer from stress related to their work.

striated muscle ► muscle

stroke *noun*

A stroke is a type of injury that affects the **brain**. It occurs when the **blood** supply is cut off from part of the brain. Strokes are caused by a blood **clot** or a burst blood vessel. People can recover fully from mild strokes. More serious strokes cause brain damage that can prevent a person from moving or speaking. Some strokes lead to a **coma** and death.

The stroke left him paralyzed down his left side.

stutter *noun*

A stutter is a **speech** disorder. A person with a stutter finds it difficult to speak fluently. The beginnings of words are said over and over again before the full word comes out. There are gaps between words and the speech is slow. A stutter can be helped with a treatment called speech therapy.

Her stutter became worse when she was embarrassed.

stye *noun*

A stye is a painful, red lump on the **eyelid**. It occurs when germs get into the root of an **eyelash** and start an **infection**. **Pus** builds up in the lump. A stye should be bathed with a clean cloth dipped in hot, sterile water. This eases the pain and helps the sty to burst.

Rubbing the eye can make a stye worse.

sucrose *noun*

Sucrose is a kind of **sugar** found in most sweet foods. The sugar used to sprinkle over food is nearly all made of sucrose. The body uses sucrose for energy, but too much sucrose in the **diet** causes dental cavities and other problems.

Some sucrose is made from sugar beets.

sugar *noun*

Sugar is a sweet substance in **food**. There are many kinds of sugars, all of which can dissolve in water and be used by the body as **energy**. All sugars are broken down by the body and turned into a blood sugar called **glucose**.

Most people enjoy eating foods with sugar.

surgery *noun*

Surgery is a branch of **medicine** that treats **disease** by carrying out **operations**. A doctor trained in surgery is called a surgeon.

The boy had surgery to remove his appendix.

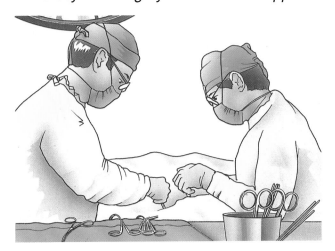

swallow *verb*

Swallow means to pass food from the mouth to the **esophagus.** After chewing, the **tongue** presses food to the back of the **throat**. A flap of skin called the **epiglottis** shuts off the **trachea**, and the food passes into the **esophagus**. This is full of strong muscles that tighten in waves and force the food down into the stomach. These muscle movements are called peristalsis.

Laughing while swallowing causes choking.

140

sweat *noun*
Sweat is a salty fluid. It is made by sweat glands in the skin and passed out to the surface through tiny openings, or **pores**. Sweating is one of the ways the body keeps cool. It also helps to get rid of urea, a waste product in **blood**. Stale sweat has a strong smell. This is caused by **bacteria** breaking down the mixture of sweat and dead cells on the surface of the **skin.**
The body loses moisture through the skin in sweat.
sweat *verb*

sweat gland *noun*
A sweat gland is a tiny tube that lies coiled under the **skin.** Sweat glands absorb fluid, salts, and urea from the **blood.** These waste products are then passed out to the surface of skin as sweat. There are sweat glands all over the body. Many of them cluster in the armpits, the soles of the feet and the palms of the hands. Sweat glands become more active during and after **puberty.**
Sweat glands produce some sweat even when a person is cool.

swell *verb*
To swell is to grow bigger. Swelling in the body is a **symptom**. It may be caused by inflamed or damaged **tissue**. A swelling that forms a lump is called a **tumor**. Swelling also occurs when fluid collects in tissue.
A sprained ankle will begin to swell.
swelling *noun*

swelling on a hand caused by rheumatism

symptom *noun*
A symptom is something unusual about a body. Symptoms can be seen, such as a swelling. Or they may be felt, such as a headache. Symptoms may be inside or outside the body, painful or not painful. Doctors ask a patient about his or her symptoms to see if they suggest **illness**.
A runny nose is a symptom of a common cold.

syndrome *noun*
A syndrome is a group of **symptoms** that point to one kind of **illness**.
His symptoms amounted to a syndrome of rheumatic fever.

syringe *noun*
A syringe is a medical instrument. At one end is a plunger that pushes down into a tube. There is a hollow needle or smaller tube at the other end. Syringes **inject** or draw out fluids, usually through the skin. They can also be used to clean wounds and wash out openings in the body, such as ears.
The nurse used a syringe to give the boy an injection.

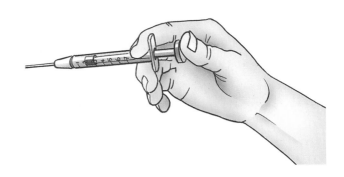

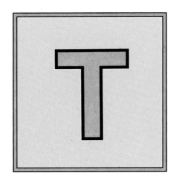

tactile *adjective*
Tactile describes anything to do with the sense of **touch**. Stroking the skin is a tactile action.
The fingers have the most highly developed tactile sense.

tapeworm *noun*
A tapeworm is a flat worm that lives inside some animals. Humans catch tapeworm by eating its eggs in undercooked beef, pork, or fish. Hooks on the worm's head cling to the wall of the **intestine**. Segments of the worm's body containing eggs fall off and pass out of the body in the **feces**. Tapeworms cause **diarrhea**, weight loss, and stomach pain. Worm-killing drugs clear tapeworm out of the body.
Tapeworms can grow to over ten feet long inside the body.

tarsals ► **foot**

tartar ► **plaque**

taste ► **tongue**

taste bud *noun*
Taste buds detect flavors in the **mouth**. Over 9,000 taste buds surround tiny bumps on the **tongue**, the back of the mouth, and the **throat**. Taste buds respond to a flavor when it has dissolved, or become liquid, in the mouth. **Nerve endings** in the taste buds pick up flavors and send the message of taste to the **brain.**
Taste buds pick up sour, sweet, bitter and salt tastes.

tears *plural noun*
Tears are a watery, salty fluid made by a gland behind the upper **eyelid**. The fluid is fed through tubes to the surface of the **eyeball**. It then drains away through two small openings in the inner corner of each **eye**. Tears protect and moisten the eye. A special **enzyme** in tears kills **germs** and helps to stop **infection**.
Blinking helps to spread tears over the eyeball.

teenage *adjective*
Teenage describes a person from 13 to 19 years of age. People pass through **puberty** and **adolescence** during their teenage years. Someone of this age is often called a teenager.
She was in high school and college all through her teenage years.

teeth ► page 144

temperature *noun*
Temperature is a measure of heat. The normal temperature inside the body is about 98.6 degrees Fahrenheit. Body temperature is controlled by a part of the **brain** called the **hypothalamus**. A rise in temperature is a **symptom** called a **fever** and is usually a sign of illness. The temperature in the body is measured with a **thermometer**.
He had a slight fever, with a temperature of 101 degrees.

Changes in body temperature (° Fahrenheit)

	unconsciousness, possible death
106	pulse rate rises
99	
97	normal body temperature
93	pulse rate falls
86	unconsciousness
77	death

tendon *noun*
A tendon is a strip of **tissue** that attaches **muscles** to **bones**. A tendon can be strained, inflamed, or even torn, by overuse.
She snapped the tendon in her ankle and could not move her foot.

tension *noun*
Tension is a strain caused by stretching. **Muscles** become tense if they are overstretched. This can lead to cramp-like pains. Tension also describes when the **mind** is overstretched by having too much to do at one time. This type of tension makes a person worried or anxious. Relaxation is the treatment for tension in the body or mind.
A hot bath can give relief for muscle tension.
tense *adjective*

testis (plural **testes**) *noun*
A testis is one of the two sex organs contained in the male's **scrotum**, the sac of skin that hangs below a **penis**. The testes are also called the testicles. In an adult, each testis is about an inch and a half long and shaped like an egg. Testes make **sperm** and a male **hormone** called testosterone. Testosterone helps a boy to develop into a man.
Mumps can cause a man's testes to become inflamed.

testicle ► **testis**

tetanus *noun*
Tetanus is a **disease** caused by **germs** that live in the soil or animal **feces**. These germs can enter the body through a cut in the skin. The first signs of tetanus are a stiff **jaw** which makes it difficult to swallow. Another name for tetanus is lockjaw. Unless it is treated, the stiffness spreads down the body and leads to spasms, **convulsions**, and usually **death**.
Vaccinations can protect people from tetanus.

thalamus (plural **thalami**) *noun*
The thalamus is one of two egg-shaped organs that lie above the **hypothalamus** in the brain. The thalami are **nerve** centers that pass messages from the eyes, ears, nose, mouth, and skin to the brain.
Sensory nerves link the mouth to the thalamus.

thermogram *noun*
Thermograms record levels of heat inside the body, using a special television camera that is sensitive to heat. The different temperatures show as different colors when printed on paper. Because levels of heat can tell doctors about what is happening inside the body, a thermogram can indicate whether there is something wrong with an **organ**.
A thermogram can reveal circulatory problems.

thermogram picture of upper body and arm

thermometer *noun*
A thermometer is an instrument that measures the **temperature** in the body. Thermometers contain a special liquid, usually a type of liquid metal called mercury, in a tube. This liquid rises up the tube when it is heated. Thermometers can be placed under the tongue, in the armpit, groin or anus. The body heat makes the liquid rise. After a few minutes, this can be measured against the scale on the side of the tube, giving the person's temperature.
The nurse placed the thermometer in his mouth to see whether he had a fever.

tooth *noun*

A tooth is a bony shell that grows out of the **gum** in the mouth. Each tooth is covered with a hard layer of **enamel** over a substance called **dentin**. The soft middle of a tooth is called the pulp and is filled with **nerves** and **blood vessels**. Teeth are used for cutting and chewing food. Children have 20 baby teeth which fall out and are replaced by 32 adult, or permanent, teeth. *Careful brushing helps keep teeth and gums healthy.*

A molar tooth

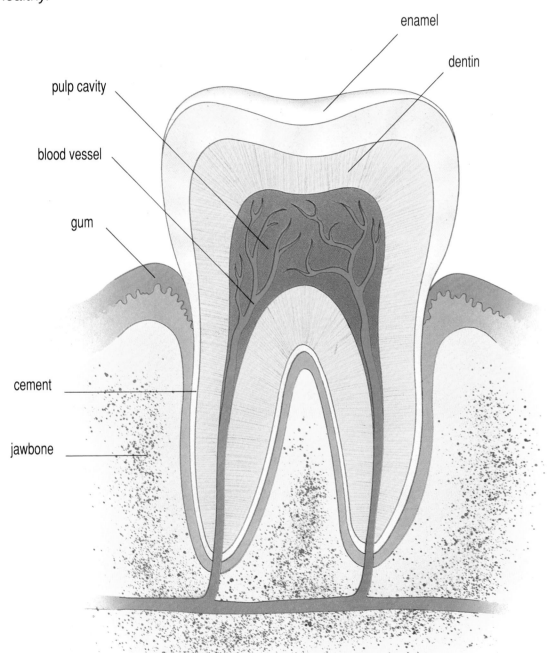

enamel

dentin

pulp cavity

blood vessel

gum

cement

jawbone

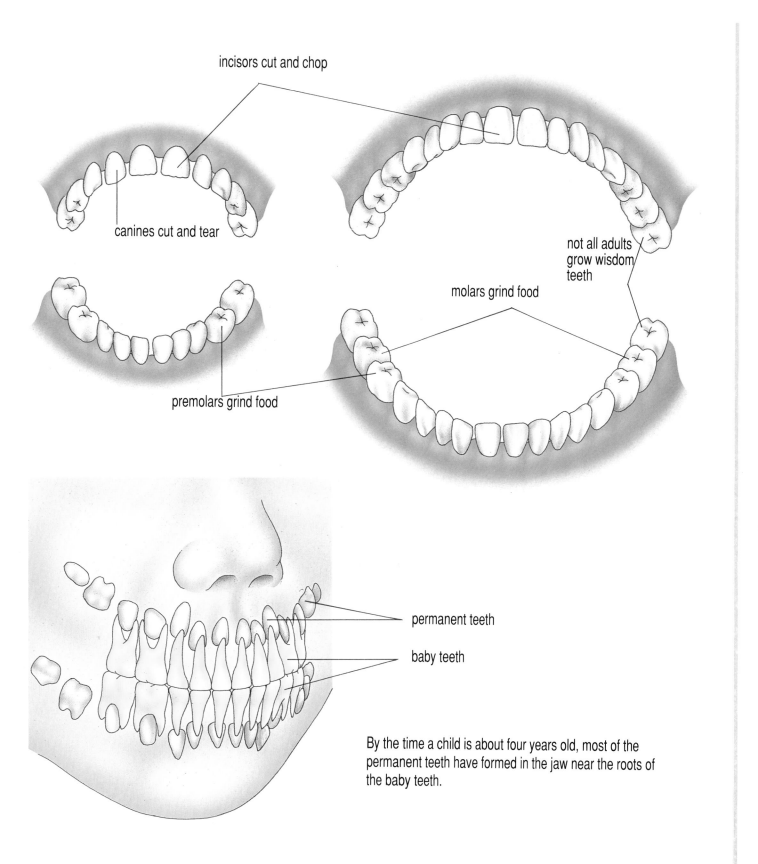

incisors cut and chop

canines cut and tear

premolars grind food

molars grind food

not all adults grow wisdom teeth

permanent teeth

baby teeth

By the time a child is about four years old, most of the permanent teeth have formed in the jaw near the roots of the baby teeth.

thigh *noun*
The thigh is the part of a **leg** between the **knee** and the **hip**. The thighbone, or **femur**, is the longest and one of the strongest bones.
Strenuous exercise gave the weightlifter extremely strong thighs.

think *verb*
To think is to form ideas, or thoughts, in the **mind**. Thinking is part of the **intellect**. Humans have greater thinking abilities than animals.
Only humans can think.

thoracic *adjective*
Thoracic describes anything to do with the **chest**.
Lungs are located in the thoracic cavity.

thorax ► chest

threadworm *noun*
A threadworm is a small worm that may live in the **large intestine**. The female worm crawls down the rectum to lay her eggs around the **anus**. This causes severe itching and can lead to **infection**.
The doctor used drugs to treat an infection caused by threadworm.

throat *noun*
The throat is the front part of the **neck**. It starts at the back of the **mouth** in the **pharynx**. The **larynx** and openings to the **esophagus** and **trachea** are all in the throat. The front outside part of a neck is also called a throat.
Large arteries pass through the throat.

thrombosis *noun*
A thrombosis is a blood **clot** that forms in an artery or vein. A clot that breaks loose and travels around a **blood vessel** is called an **embolus**. Thrombosis prevents blood flowing properly and causes a blockage.
A coronary thrombosis results in damage to the heart muscle.

thumb *noun*
The thumb is the first **finger** on each **hand**. Thumbs are shorter and fatter than other fingers and only have two bones, whereas the other four fingers each have three. The base of each thumb has a **joint** unlike any other in the body. These unusual joints, called saddle joints, allow thumbs to move from side to side and backward and forward.
Because the human thumb can push against the fingers it is called an opposable thumb.

thymus *noun*
A thymus is an **organ** in the **chest**, located above and in front of the **heart**. The thymus makes **white blood cells** which help to protect the body from illness. Babies are born with a large thymus, which gradually doubles in size during childhood. After **puberty** the thymus starts to shrink and is less active.
The thymus forms part of the lymphatic system.

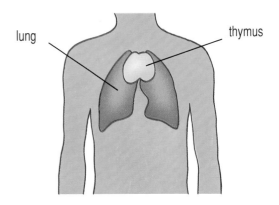

lung   thymus

thyroid gland *noun*
The thyroid gland is an **organ** in the neck, located around the front and sides of the **trachea** just below the **larynx**. The thyroid gland releases **hormones** into the blood that affect all the cells in the body. These hormones control how quickly the body burns energy. This is known as the **metabolic rate** of the body.
Hormones from the thyroid gland are important for a child's mental development.

tibia *noun*
A tibia is the longer of the two bones in the lower leg. The thinner, outer bone is called the **fibula**. The top of the tibia forms part of the **knee**. The lower end forms part of the **ankle**.
The tibia is also called the shinbone.

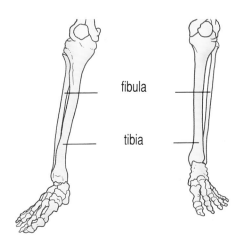

fibula

tibia

tic *noun*
A tick is a rapid twitching of a muscle that a person cannot control. Tics often occur in the muscles of the face.
The boy's blinking eye was an annoying tic.

tick *noun*
A tick is a small animal that sucks **blood**. Some ticks have soft bodies and others have hard, shell-like backs. Ticks bury their heads in the **skin** of a human or animal to feed. Some kinds of tick carry **disease**, such as Lyme disease. A tick should be dabbed with alcohol before carefully removing with tweezers. Pulling at it may leave the head behind and cause **infection**.
Ticks swell up as they feed on blood.

tinnitus *noun*
Tinnitus is a sound heard inside the **ear**. It may be a ringing, buzzing or hissing noise. Tinnitus may be caused by wax in the ear, or head or ear injuries. Tinnitus may be linked with **deafness**.
Tinnitus kept him awake at night.

tissue *noun*
Tissue is the fabric of the body. Clumps of **cells** of the same kind are arranged in layers to form tissue. Different types of cell are grouped together to make **skin** and every other **organ** in the body. Living tissue is fed with **oxygen** and **nutrients** from blood. Dead tissue, such as hair, has no blood supply.
The tissue round her sprained wrist was swollen and puffy.

toe *noun*
A toe is found at the end of a **foot**. There are five toes ending in five toenails on each foot. The big toe has only two bones, like the **thumb** of each hand. Each of the other toes has three bones. Toe bones, or **phalanges**, are joined together by **joints** that act like hinges and allow them to bend. Toes help to spread the weight of the body evenly. They also help the body to **balance** on the feet.
When he broke his toe, he found it very difficult to walk.

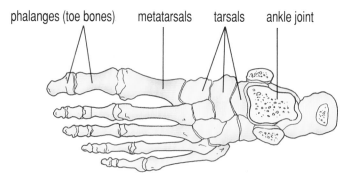

phalanges (toe bones)   metatarsals   tarsals   ankle joint

tongue ▶ page 148

tonsil *noun*
A tonsil is a lump of spongy **tissue** at the back of the **mouth**. There are two main tonsils that lie on either side of the entrance to the **throat**. Tonsils help to prevent **germs** from getting into the throat. Sometimes tonsils become infected. When this happens, they are surgically removed by a simple operation.
Children have bigger tonsils than adults.

tongue   *noun*

The tongue is a muscular **organ** in the **mouth**. It is attached to the back and the floor of the mouth. The tip of the tongue is free to move all around and out of the mouth. Tongues are covered with moist, bumpy skin. Thousands of **taste buds** on the surface of the tongue pick up flavors in food and drink. Tongues are used to push food into the **pharynx**. Movements of the tongue also help to make the sounds of **speech**.

The number of taste buds in the tongue decreases as a person gets older.

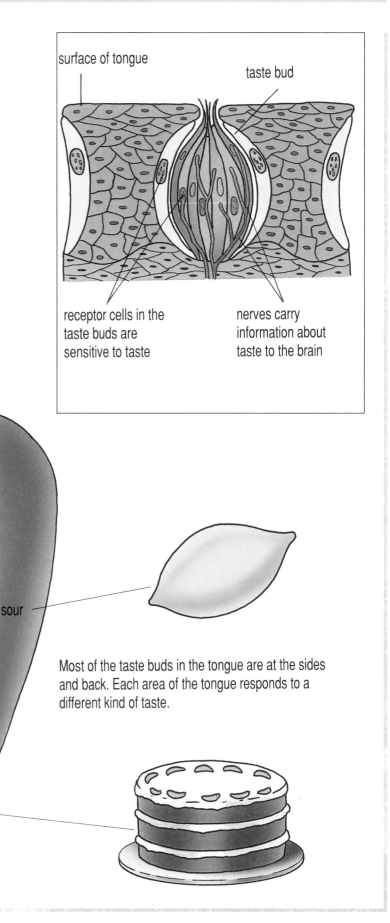

surface of tongue

taste bud

receptor cells in the taste buds are sensitive to taste

nerves carry information about taste to the brain

bitter

sour

sour

salt

salt

sweet

Most of the taste buds in the tongue are at the sides and back. Each area of the tongue responds to a different kind of taste.

tonsillitis *noun*

Tonsillitis is a common childhood **illness** that occurs when the tonsils are infected by **bacteria**. The **throat** becomes sore and swollen. There may be a headache and fever. Tonsillitis is treated with **antibiotic drugs** that kill the germs causing the infection. If tonsillitis keeps coming back, the tonsils can be surgically removed to cure the problem.
Her tonsillitis was so bad that she could hardly swallow.

tooth ► teeth

toothache *noun*

Toothache is a pain in a tooth, or around a tooth. It is usually caused by decay. Decay eats away the hard, outer layer of a tooth. When the **nerve** inside is exposed, a person feels toothache. Most toothache is cured by filling or removing the tooth.
He took a painkiller to relieve his toothache.

touch ► page 150

toxin *noun*

A toxin is a poison made in the **cells** of animals and plants. If they enter the body, as in an infection or a bite, the body fights toxins by producing **antitoxins** in the blood. Specially treated toxins are sometimes given to people as **vaccines**.
The venom of a poisonous snake is a kind of toxin.
toxic *adjective*

trachea *noun*

The trachea is the air passage from the **larynx** in the throat to the lungs. It runs from the **throat** down to just above the **heart** in the middle of the **chest**. Here it divides into two tubes, or **bronchi**, that lead to each **lung**. A flap of skin called the **epiglottis** closes the top of the trachea when a person swallows.
The trachea of an adult is about five inches long.

transfusion *noun*

A transfusion is a way of giving a person **blood**. Fresh blood from a healthy person is fed through a hollow needle into a **vein**. Transfusions are given to people who do not have enough blood because of an accident or disease. The blood they are given must be of a **blood group** compatible with their own. **Plasma** is also given by transfusion.
Blood given by donors for transfusion can be stored in a blood bank until it is needed.

transplant *noun*

A transplant is a way of taking an **organ** or part of the body from one person, or donor, and putting it into another person, or recipient. Some organs, such as the heart, are taken from people who have recently died. Sometimes, a living donor gives part of the body that he or she can live without, such as one kidney. For a successful transplant, the body **tissue** of the donor and the recipient must be of a similar type. In this way, the recipient's body does not reject the transplanted organ.
Her sight improved dramatically after the corneal transplant.

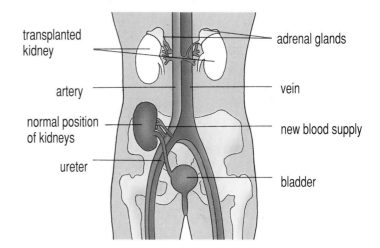

trauma *noun*

Trauma is a medical word for an injury or wound. It can also be emotional **shock** caused by an accident or great unhappiness.
She suffered trauma after the horrific train wreck.

touch *noun*

Touch is a **sense**. It is being able to feel something when the **skin** comes in contact with it. **Sensory nerves** in the skin send messages to the **brain**. Some parts of the body, such as fingertips and lips, are very sensitive to touch. This is because the skin that covers them has more nerve endings than other parts of the body.

Blind people often have a specially sensitive sense of touch.

There are different kinds of nerve endings in the skin.

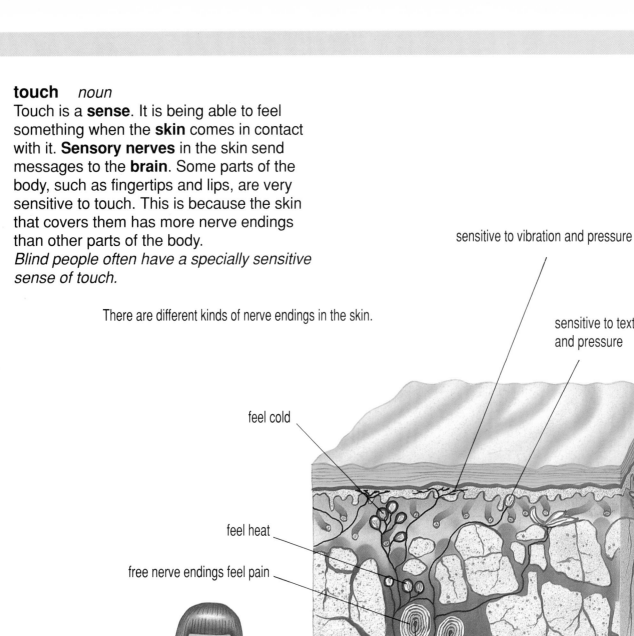

sensitive to vibration and pressure

sensitive to texture and pressure

feel cold

feel heat

free nerve endings feel pain

If all the skin's nerve endings were equally spaced, the body would look very different

treatment *noun*
Treatment is the care of **illness**. Giving drugs and other kinds of **medicine** is often part of treatment. Resting is another way of treating illness. The treatment for a small cut is to clean it, put on antiseptic and a bandage. Some treatment, such as an **operation**, is carried out in a **hospital**.
The doctor said the best treatment was to rest and drink plenty of fluids.

triceps *noun*
A triceps is a **muscle** that lies along the back of the upper **arm** and helps to move the forearm. This strong muscle works with the **biceps** muscle on the front of the upper arm. The triceps tightens to move the arm into a straight line. The biceps tightens to bend the arm at the **elbow**. When one muscle is tight and short the other is long and relaxed.
The triceps works with the biceps to move the forearm.

trichinosis *noun*
Trichinosis is an **illness** caused by tiny, round worms that live inside the **stomach**, **intestine**, and **muscles**. These kinds of worm get into the body when a person eats undercooked pork. Diarrhea and vomiting are the first **symptoms**. Two weeks later the eyelids swell and the skin covering the eyeball becomes red and inflamed. Aching muscles, fever, and weakness follow.
Trichinosis can be prevented by cooking pork thoroughly.

tuberculosis *noun*
Tuberculosis is an infectious **disease** caused by **bacteria**. It attacks the **lungs** and may then spread to other parts of the body. There are fevers, night sweats, and weight loss. A person coughs up blood as the lungs become more damaged. **Antibiotic drugs** cure tuberculosis. There is also a **vaccine** that protects people from catching this disease.
In the past, tuberculosis used to be called consumption.

tumor *noun*
A tumor is a **swelling** in the body. This can be any kind of lump, such as an **abscess** or **cyst**. A tumor may be a growth of **tissue** that is harmless, or **benign**. A tumor may also be **malignant** and a symptom of **cancer**. A malignant tumor needs to be removed before it spreads to other parts of the body. All swellings should be seen by a doctor.
She was relieved that her tumor was benign.

twins *plural noun*
Twins are two **babies** who grow in the **uterus** at the same time. The babies are born one after the other. Identical twins result when a fertilized **ovum** divides in two. The two ova develop into two babies of the same sex who look alike. Nonidentical, or fraternal, twins occur when two ova are fertilized by two sperm. These babies may be different sexes, and they look no more alike than any other brother or sister.
Fraternal twins tend to run in families.

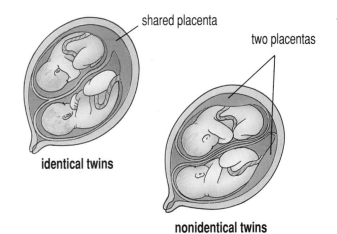
shared placenta
two placentas
identical twins
nonidentical twins

typhoid fever *noun*
Typhoid fever is a kind of food poisoning caused by **bacteria** in the **intestine**. This causes a high fever, constipation, and a **rash** over the chest and abdomen. Diarrhea and more serious illness may follow. Typhoid is carried in food and water contaminated by feces or urine. **Antibiotic drugs** are used to treat this disease.
People who have recovered from typhoid may still carry and pass on the infection.

typhus *noun*
Typhus is a general term for a group of **diseases** carried by rat fleas, lice, ticks, and mites in areas where the standard of **hygiene** is low. Two weeks after a bite from one of these blood-sucking insects, a person develops a severe headache and a high fever. A pink **rash** breaks out over most of the body. **Vaccines** can help protect people from some forms of typhus.
The spread of typhus can be controlled by killing the insects that carry the disease.

ulcer *noun*
An ulcer is an open sore. Ulcers may develop on the inside or on the outside of the body. There are many different kinds of ulcer. Some are mild and heal quickly, such as those caused by a scrape or a burn. Others are **symptoms** of a more serious illness. Ulcers that develop inside the **stomach**, such as a peptic ulcer, may take a long time to heal.
Her mouth ulcer hurt from the acid in the tomato.
ulcerous *adjective*

ulna *noun*
An ulna is a **bone** in the lower **arm** that runs from the back of the elbow to the **wrist**. The top end of the ulna joins the bone of the upper arm, called the **humerus**, to form part of the **elbow**. The lower end forms part of the wrist on the side of the little finger. The other bone in the arm is the **radius**.
The ulna twists over the radius to allow the wrist to turn.

ultrasound *noun*
Ultrasound is sound waves that are too high to be detected by the human **ear**. Ultrasound can be passed into the body in a thin beam. Because solid objects, such as **bone**, reflect the sound waves, while less dense **tissue** and **organs** absorb them, the echo from ultrasound can be used form an image of the inside of the body. Ultrasound is a safe method of examining the **fetus** in early **pregnancy**.
The ultrasound picture showed that the baby's spine was normal.

umbilical cord   *noun*

An umbilical cord is a coil of **blood vessels** surrounded by **skin** that joins a mother to the fetus in the **uterus**. One end of the cord is attached to the middle of the baby's **abdomen**. The other end joins the **placenta** on the wall of the uterus. **Oxygen** and **nutrients** pass through the placenta and cord to the baby. After **childbirth**, the cord is cut. The stump shrivels and falls off, leaving a scar called a **navel.**

The umbilical cord is usually about 2 feet long.

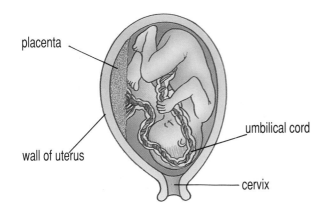

placenta

wall of uterus

umbilical cord

cervix

unconscious   *adjective*

To be unconscious is to be not awake. A person may be fully unconscious after a head injury. This looks like a deep **sleep.** Or a person may be semi-conscious, or half awake, such as when he or she is recovering from a fit or a **faint**. Someone who is deeply unconscious through accident or illness is said to be in a **coma.**

She was knocked unconscious when the brick hit her head.

ureter   *noun*

A ureter is one of two thin tubes in the body. The top end of each ureter is attached to a **kidney**. The lower ends join the **bladder**. **Urine** drains into the ureters from the kidneys and is passed into the bladder. Muscles in the ureters help to squeeze the urine down.

The muscles in the ureters contract and relax about three times a minute.

urethra   *noun*

The urethra is the narrow tube from the bladder through which **urine** is passed out of the body. The urethra in a male travels down the **penis** into an opening at the end. The male urethra also acts as a passage for **semen**. The opening of the female urethra lies between the **vagina** and the **clitoris**. *A man's urethra is much longer than a woman's.*

urine   *noun*

Urine is a fluid made in the body. It is mostly water mixed with salts and **waste products**, such as urea, filtered from the **blood**. Urine is made by the **kidneys** and carried to the **bladder** by the **ureters**, where it is stored. It is then passed out of the body as a waste product. Normally, urine is a yellow color. *Eating beets can change the color of urine from yellow to reddish.*

urine test   *noun*

A urine test looks for substances in the **urine**. A small amount of urine is mixed with chemicals, to see whether there is anything unusual in the urine, such as **blood** or **pus**. Urine tests can tell a doctor if a person has a certain kind of illness, such as **diabetes**, because one of the symptoms of diabetes is sugar in the urine. A urine test can also show if a woman is pregnant. *The urine test showed that she had a small amount of glucose in her urine.*

uterus   *noun*

The uterus is the strong, pear-shaped **organ** that lies in a woman's **pelvis** at the top of the **vagina.** Unborn babies grow in the uterus, which becomes bigger during **pregnancy**. Every month after **puberty** the uterus grows a thick lining in case a woman becomes pregnant. If no **ovum** is fertilized, the lining is shed and passed out of the body during **menstruation**.

The uterus is also called the womb.
uterine   *adjective*

153

uvula *noun*
The uvula is the small, soft lump of **tissue** that hangs from the soft **palate** at the back of the mouth. It dangles over the entrance to the **throat** and can be seen when the mouth is opened wide and the **tongue** held down.
The singer opened his mouth so wide, everyone could see his uvula.

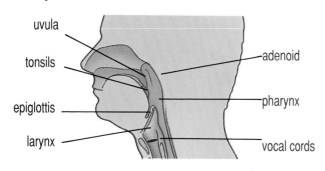

uvula
tonsils
adenoid
epiglottis
pharynx
larynx
vocal cords

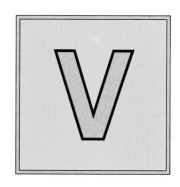

vaccination *noun*
A vaccination is a dose of **medicine** made from a **vaccine**. Vaccinations are given by mouth or by an injection through the skin. Vaccinations prevent all kinds of **disease**, such as **measles**, **diphtheria**, and **smallpox**. Many people are given vaccinations in childhood.
The doctor recommended he should have a tetanus vaccination every 10 years.

vaccine *noun*
A vaccine is a **medicine** that stops people from catching a **disease**. It is made from specially treated samples of the **germs** that cause the disease. These may be living or dead. Giving someone a vaccine makes the body's defense, or **immune system**, attack the germs. The person then has immunity, or protection from this disease without ever catching it.
The poliomyelitis vaccine may be given as drops into a baby's mouth.

vagina *noun*
The vagina is a female sex organ. It is the passage between the **vulva** and **uterus** inside the body. The opening of the vagina lies between the **urethra** and the **anus** between the legs. The soft, elastic walls of the vagina fold together with the action of **muscles**. They are covered with a moist **membrane**, which helps to keep the vagina clean and free from germs. A woman's vagina is about three inches long.
During childbirth, the baby passes out of the uterus and through the vagina.
vaginal *adjective*

valve *noun*
A valve is a flap of **tissue** in a tube that prevents a liquid from flowing backward. Valves in the **veins** and **heart** make sure **blood** flows in the right direction. Another valve in the body lies between the small and the large **intestine**. This stops liquid food from moving backward.
The semilunar valve in the heart has three flaps shaped like half moons.

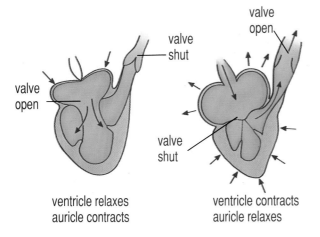

valve open

valve shut

valve open

valve shut

ventricle relaxes auricle contracts

ventricle contracts auricle relaxes

vein *noun*
A vein is a tube inside the body that carries **blood** back to the **heart**. Tiny veins called **capillaries** pass the blood to larger veins called venules. These join bigger veins that connect up to two huge veins that empty blood into the heart. The blood flow in a vein is helped by the muscles that surround it. The blood can flow only one way because many of the veins are fitted with **valves**.
Veins have thinner walls than arteries.
venous *adjective*

ventricle *noun*
A ventricle is a space in the **heart**. It is one of the two lower **cavities**, or chambers, that pump **blood** into the **arteries** during **circulation**. The right ventricle pumps blood to the **lungs**. The left ventricle pumps blood to the **arteries**. The ventricles receive blood from the **atria**, the two upper chambers of the heart.
The ventricles of the heart are stronger than the atria.

verruca *noun*
A verruca is another name for a **wart**, which is a skin infection due to a **virus**.
The verruca on the sole of his foot was quite painful.

vertebra (plural **vertebrae**) *noun*
A vertebra is a **bone** in the **spine**. There are 33 vertebrae in the backbone, from the **neck** down to the **coccyx**. The smallest vertebrae are in the neck, and they get bigger farther down the spine. The upper 24 vertebrae are cushioned between strong **discs** of **cartilage**. These flexible, ring-shaped bones surround and protect the **spinal cord**.
The lowest four vertebrae are fused together to form the coccyx.

vertebrate *adjective*
Vertebrate describes an animal that has a **backbone**.
Rabbits and snakes are examples of vertebrate animals.

vertigo *noun*
Vertigo is a disorder of **balance**. It is the feeling of spinning around when a person stays still or sometimes objects outside the body seem to be spinning around. People with vertigo often feel **nauseous**. Vertigo may be caused by a blockage or infection in the **ear**. Alcohol and **drugs** sometimes cause vertigo. It may also be a sign of other illness. A person suffering from vertigo should lie down with the eyes closed.
Climbing to the top of the tower gave him a bad attack of vertigo.

virus *noun*
A virus is a tiny **germ** that can be seen only with a powerful microscope. Viruses are much smaller than **bacteria**. They survive only in living **tissue**, infecting cells. Different viruses attack different kinds of cells in the body. Many diseases, such as measles and influenza, are caused by viruses. **Vaccines** protect people from some of these diseases.
The common cold is caused by a virus.

voice   *noun*

The voice is sound made by the **vocal cords**. Part of the **larynx** in the throat, the two vocal cords are folds of skin with a gap between them called the **glottis**. The voice is produced when air from the **lungs** pushes past the vocal cords, making them vibrate. Voices enable people to speak, sing, and make noises.

After puberty, male voices sound lower than female voices.

Vocal cords seen from above, looking down throat

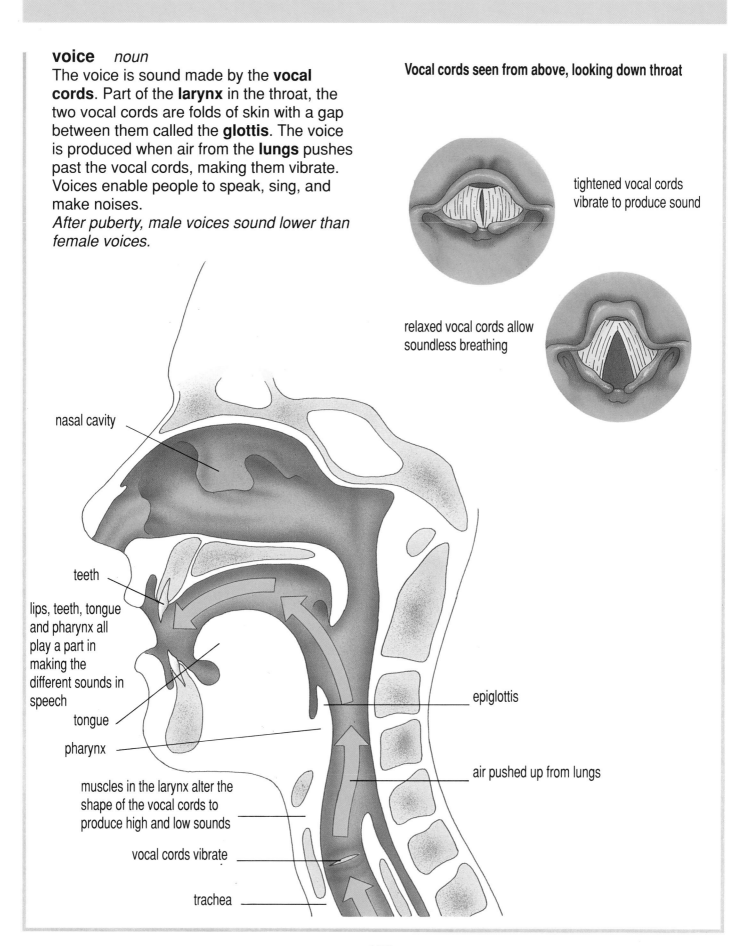

tightened vocal cords vibrate to produce sound

relaxed vocal cords allow soundless breathing

nasal cavity

teeth

lips, teeth, tongue and pharynx all play a part in making the different sounds in speech

tongue

pharynx

muscles in the larynx alter the shape of the vocal cords to produce high and low sounds

vocal cords vibrate

trachea

epiglottis

air pushed up from lungs

vision ► **sight**

vitamin   *noun*
A vitamin is a chemical substance. The body needs small amounts of all the different vitamins to grow and stay healthy. Some vitamins are known by letters of the alphabet. These are A, B, C, D, E, and K. Most vitamins are found in different kinds of **food**. Eating a balanced **diet** usually gives a person all the vitamins he or she needs.
Oranges and many other fruits are high in vitamin C.

vitiligo   *noun*
Vitiligo is a **skin** disorder in which small patches of pale-colored skin appear on the body because of a lack of **melanin**.
Sitting in the sun helped to cure her vitiligo.

vitreous humor ► **eyeball**

vocal cord   *noun*
A vocal cord is part of the **larynx** in the throat. The two vocal cords are folds of skin with a narrow space between them called the **glottis**. Air passes between the vocal cords when a person breathes. When the cords move together, the glottis becomes a tiny slit, which makes the vocal cords vibrate as air passes through.
Vibrating vocal cords make the sounds of speech and song.

voice ► page 156

voice box ► **larynx**

vomit   *verb*
To vomit is to throw up **food** from the **stomach** back out of the mouth. The vomited food is usually sour smelling and semi-liquid. Vomiting is a common **symptom** of many kinds of mild and serious illness. Food poisoning and **gastroenteritis** cause vomiting.
He vomited after he had eaten the infected shellfish.

vulva   *noun*
The vulva is the outer sex organ of a female. The soft, padded triangle at the top of the vulva is called the mons pubis. Further down the vulva are folds of skin called **labia**. These surround the **clitoris** and the openings of the **urethra** and **vagina**. The entrance to the vagina is sometimes partly covered by a fold of skin called the hymen.
The vulva grows hair and changes shape and color during puberty.

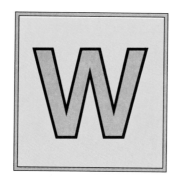

wart *noun*

A wart is a knobby growth on the **skin**, caused by a **virus**. Warts vary in size, shape and color. They are not usually painful, and they disappear in their own time if left alone. But if a plantar wart, or **verruca**, on the sole of the foot is painful, it can be removed.
The idea that people catch warts from frogs is not true.

waste product *noun*

A waste product is a substance not needed by the body. Waste products are either made in the body or taken in by the body. Some **organs**, such as the **kidney**, collect and destroy waste products. Many waste products are passed out of the body as **feces** and **urine**. Breathing out gets rid of a waste product in the air called **carbon dioxide**. **Sweating** helps the body to get rid of a waste product in the **blood** called urea.
If waste products are not removed from the body, a person can become ill.

wax *noun*

Wax is a sticky, yellow substance made in the **ear**. Wax helps to protect the ear from **infection**. Wax sometimes builds up and forms a hard plug over the **eardrum**, which may cause temporary **deafness**. The hard wax can be softened and removed by a doctor.
His hearing improved after the doctor removed the hard wax from his ears.

white blood cell ► blood cell

white matter ► brain

whooping cough *noun*

Whooping cough is a childhood **disease** caused by **bacteria** spread by the coughing of an infected person. Violent, short coughs are followed by a deep intake of breath, which makes the "whoop" sound. Whooping cough causes vomiting, and can lead to **pneumonia** and **brain** damage. It may take several months to recover from the disease.
Doctors recommend that all children be vaccinated against whooping cough.

windpipe ► trachea

wisdom tooth ► tooth

womb ► uterus

worm *noun*

A worm is an animal with a long, soft body and no legs. Different kinds of worm, called parasites, live inside humans. **Tapeworm** and **hookworm** are two kinds of worm parasites. Children sometimess catch tiny threadworms that can be seen wriggling in their **feces**. These are soon cleared out of the body with worm-killing medicines.
The worms made the boy itch round the anus.

wrist *noun*

A wrist is the part of the body that joins the **hand** to the **arm**. The wrist has eight small **bones** in two rows. The bones of the wrist meet the bones of the forearm and hand to form the wrist.
More than 20 tendons link the wrist, the arm, and the hand.

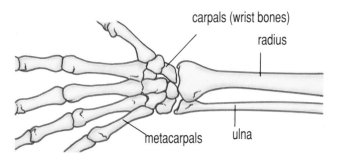

carpals (wrist bones)
radius
metacarpals
ulna

X-chromosome   *noun*
An X-chromosome is one of the two **chromosomes** that determine whether a person is **male** or **female**. The other is called a **Y-chromosome**. If there are two X-chromosomes in a fertilized **ovum**, the baby will be a girl.
Some diseases are caused by defects of the X-chromosome.

X-ray   *noun*
An X-ray is a kind of photograph of the inside of the body. X-ray pictures are black-and-white images of **bones** and **organs**. In an X-ray, the solid areas look light and the spaces in between look dark. Taking X-rays is a branch of medicine called **radiology**.
The X-ray showed a fractured tibia.

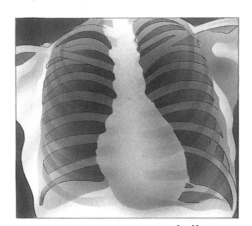

An X-ray

yaws   *noun*
Yaws is a **disease** found in tropical countries. It is caused by a **bacterium**. Soft **swellings** appear on the lips, elbows, knees, and buttocks. They break open and heal slowly. The sores may damage tissue and bones underneath the skin. The disease may disappear for several years before coming back. Yaws can be cured with **antibiotic** drugs.
The germ that causes yaws can infect another person only through broken skin.

Y-chromosome   *noun*
A Y-chromosome is one of the two **chromosomes** that determine whether a person is **male** or **female**. The other is called a **X-chromosome**. If a **sperm** carrying a Y-chromosome meets an X-chromosome in an **ovum**, the baby will be a boy. If the sperm has an X-chromosome, the baby will be a girl.
A Y-chromosome looks different from all the other chromosomes in a cell.

yellow fever   *noun*
Yellow fever is a **disease** of tropical areas caused by a **virus**, passed on by a mosquito bite. A high **fever** follows shaking chills, headache, and pains inside the body. Many people recover after these **symptoms**, but others become more ill as the **virus** attacks the **kidneys** and **liver**. This turns the skin yellow, giving the disease its name. A small number of people who catch yellow fever fall into a coma and die.
Yellow fever vaccine gives people immunity from the disease for 10 years.

yoga   *noun*
Yoga is a way of keeping fit and **healthy**.
Yoga exercises make the body strong and
supple, which means it is able to bend and
stretch easily. In yoga, the exercises are
done with a special form of breathing.
Because yoga helps people feel calm and
relaxed, it is very good for stress.
People in India have been doing yoga for
about 2,000 years.